HOW TO PLAY
TRUMPET

This book is dedicated with affectionate memories to my first great teacher, the late E. M. 'Bert' Collier,

Photo: EVENING ECHO

and
– to Tommy McQuater, the master.
– to Elizabeth, who made this book possible.
– to Ena and John, who made it *all* possible.

Instruments by courtesy of PROFESSIONAL BRASS LTD. London NW5

HOW TO PLAY
TRUMPET

Digby Fairweather

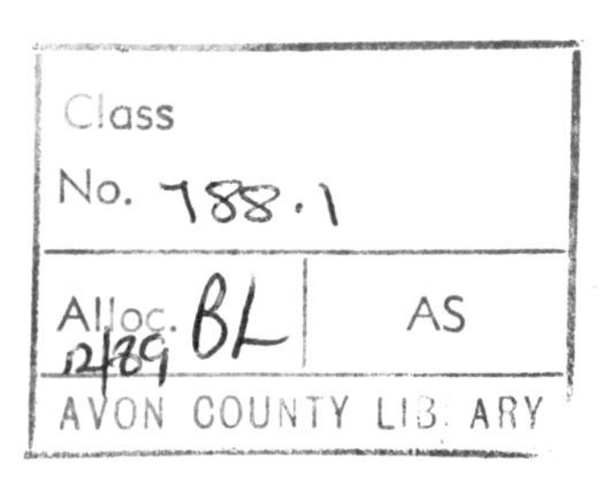

Elm Tree Books
International Music Publications

First published in Great Britain 1985
by Elm Tree Books Ltd
Garden House, 57-59 Long Acre, London WC2E 9JZ

in association with

International Music Publications
Southend Road, Woodford Green, Essex IG8 8HN

British Library Cataloguing in Publication Data

Fairweather, Digby
How to play trumpet.
1. Trumpet – Methods
I. Title
788'.1 MT442

ISBN 0-241-11528-0
ISBN 0-241-11527-2 Pbk

Printed in Great Britain by
William Clowes Ltd., Beccles and London

It's coming up to fifty years since my mother and I went to a music shop in the Charing Cross Road, London, and she handed over £4 to buy me a brand new Manhattan trumpet, complete with case, a trumpet 'tutor' *and* one free lesson on the premises! I spent two days and nights without sleep, practising the scale of C or just fingering the valves and striking Louis Armstrong poses in front of the bedroom mirror.

Allowing for adjustment in the price, I'm sure this has been a common enough experience for would-be musicians over the years. The lucky ones retain vestiges of that first infatuation throughout their lives. Louis Armstrong's biographer, Max Jones, noted that when anyone visited Louis, either in his hotel or theatre dressingroom, the trumpet was invariably out of its case and within his reach. 'Me and the horn have fallen out many times', Louis told an interviewer. 'But we manage to stay friends!'

Staying friends with the trumpet is hardest in the early stages, when there is hard and often boring work to be done, with some fairly unrewarding noises to show for it. It takes a patient, understanding and, above all, enthusiastic teacher to keep the peace, and it's unusual to find those qualities in a printed 'tutor'.

Digby Fairweather brings to the task the same zestful enthusiasm that distinguishes his own playing. Reading through his manuscript, I found myself wanting to get back to some practice – and I've been at it for half a century. I was lucky at the outset. The give-away 'tutor' that came with my Manhattan was by a musician whose own eager and adventurous style infected both Digby and myself – our mutual idol, Nat Gonella. It's nice to know that the same good luck will be handed on to anyone who starts the journey with this book in hand.

Humphrey Lyttelton

A message from Digby

'How to play the trumpet' is a comprehensive tutor-guide for beginners. Because it covers a lot of ground in a short space it may take you only a day to read — but remember that learning to play well may take years. So take your time working through the text — ten minutes practice regularly every day is enough to begin with — and never tackle a new playing unit too soon. Slow steady and organised progress is the best kind.

A lifetime of fine playing will be the reward.

Good luck.

Digby Fairweather.

Alfred Noyes

Contents

UNIT 1

The Trumpet

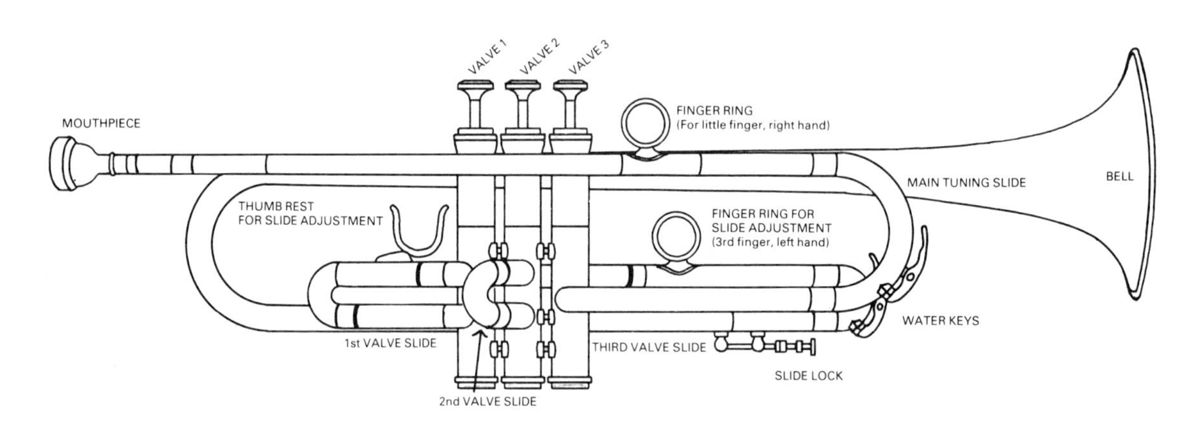

The Cornet

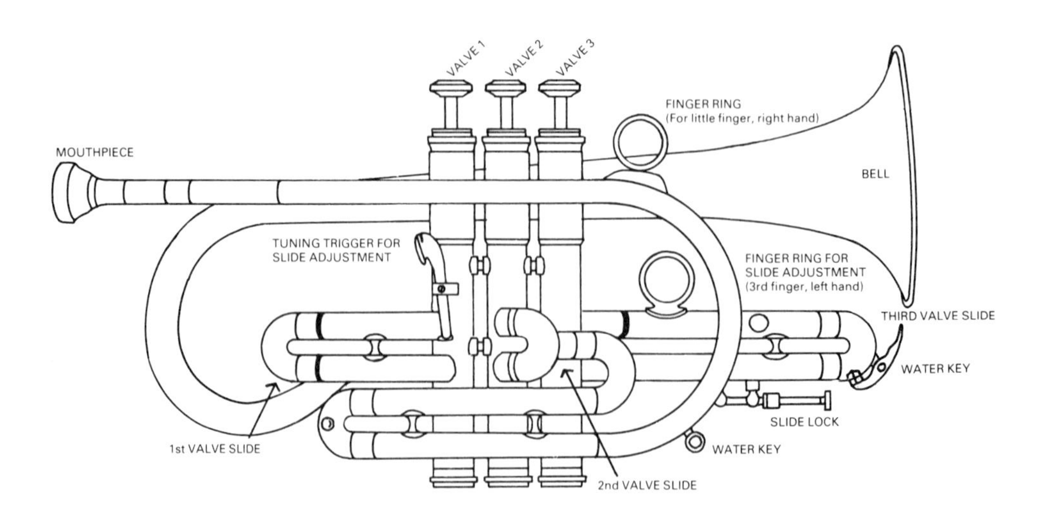

How it works

The trumpet is really just a shaped length of metal pipe. Air blown between the player's lips and through the mouthpiece at one end sets the air in the pipe moving, and this produces notes (called open notes because they're produced without pushing the valves down) by the player tightening and relaxing his lip muscles. These are the open notes:

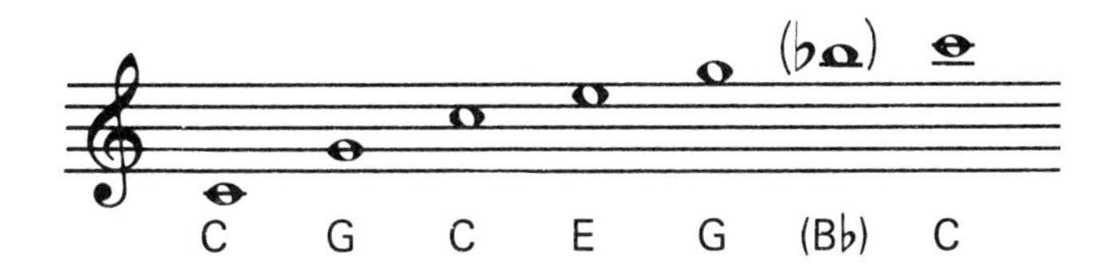

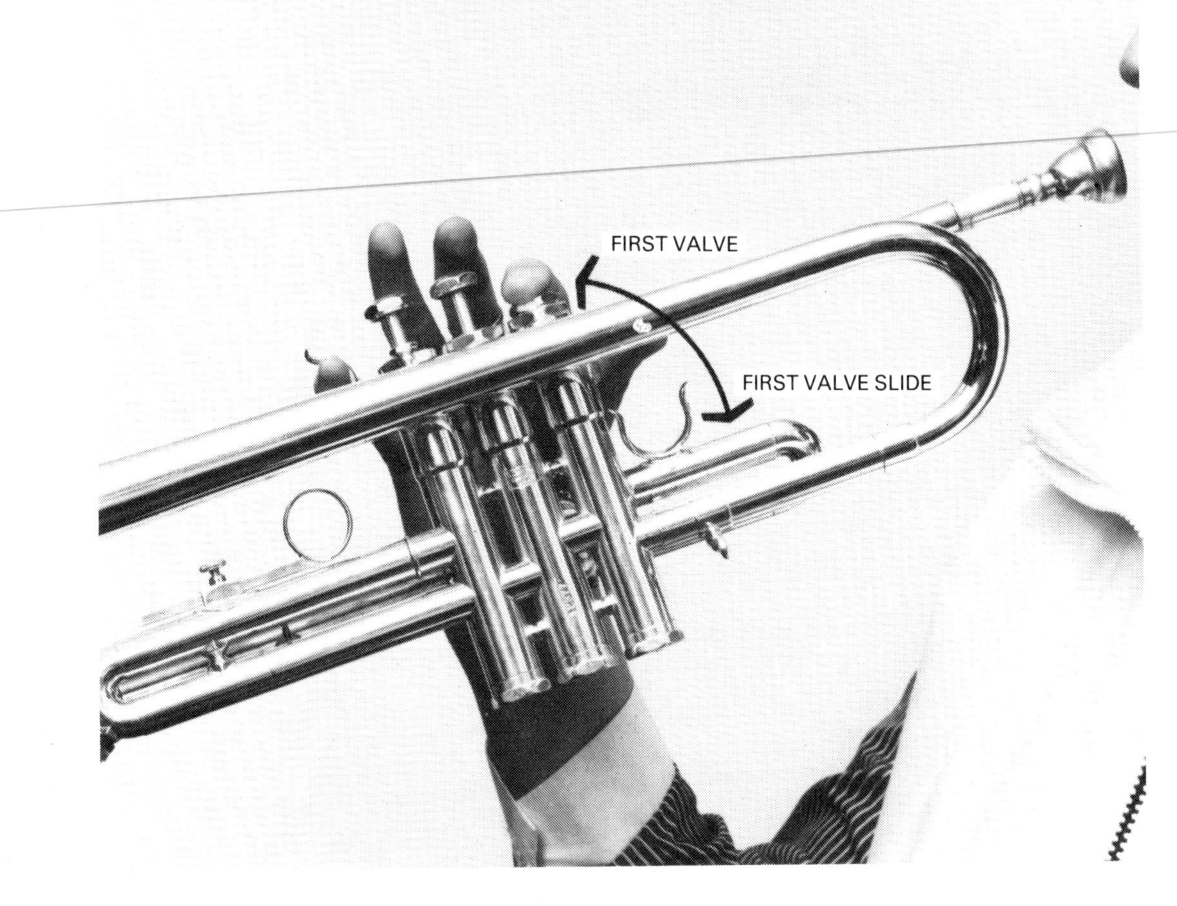

To produce the notes in between the open notes we use the valves.

Pressing down a valve opens the way to a further length of tubing (called a valve slide) through which the air must pass before it carries on through the trumpet — and this makes the note lower (a longer pipe equals a lower note — think of a church organ!). So, pressing down valve 1 opens the trumpet's first valve slide – both arrowed above – and this lowers any open note by one tone. So C for example becomes Bb.

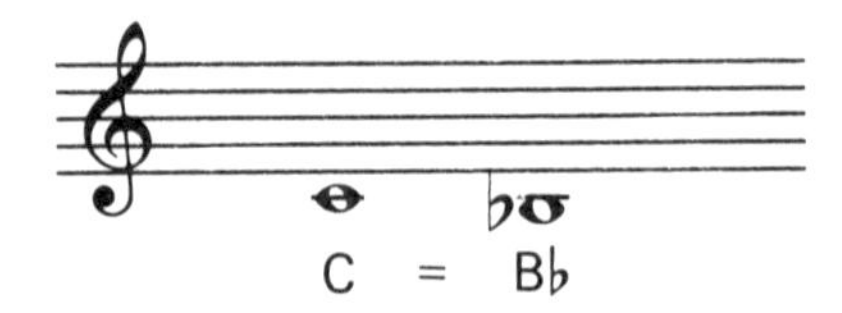

and by tightening or relaxing the lip muscles we can play:

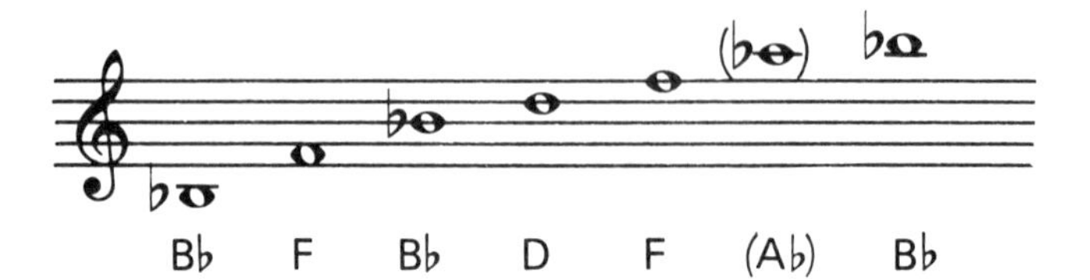

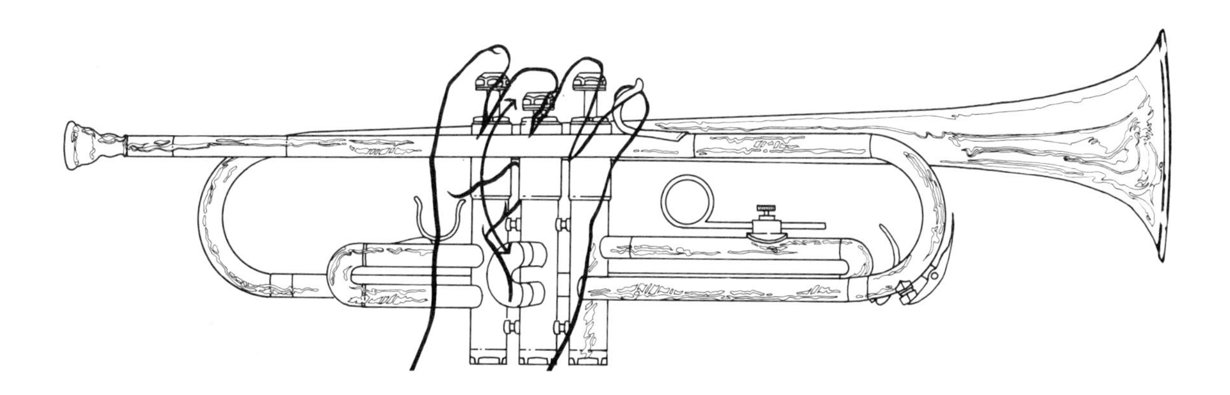

Pressing down valve 2 opens the (short) second valve slide – both arrowed above – which will lower any of the open notes by half a tone (one semitone).

So C becomes B and by using our lip muscles we can play:

B F♯ B D♯ F♯ (A) B

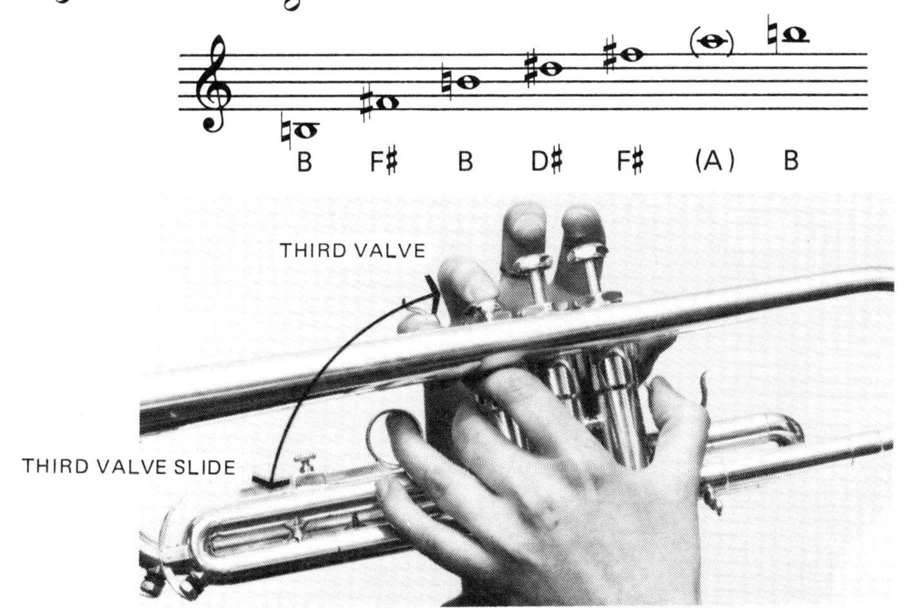

Pressing down valve 3 opens the (longest) third valve slide – both arrowed above – which will lower any of the trumpet's open notes by one and a half tones (a minor third) so C becomes A and by using our lip muscles we can play:

Using all three valves in combinations produces seven alternatives, and by using all these (*and* the open notes *and* the lip muscles) you can play all the notes in all the scales — and on the trumpet! (However, some of these notes are produced by different 'legitimate' fingering.) Exactly the same principle applies to all the trumpet family — and to brass instruments in general.

Trumpet or Cornet – Which should I choose?

TRUMPET

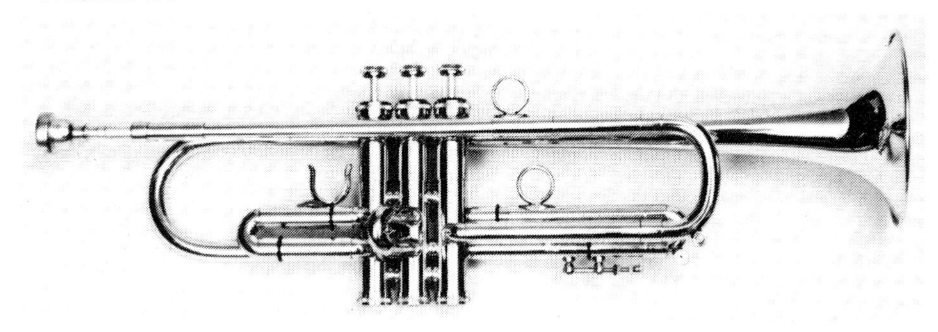

CORNET

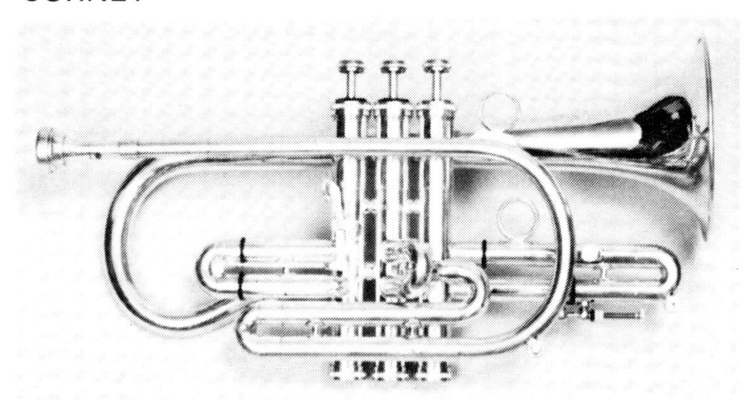

You can learn all the basic rules equally well on either, and changing over, at least early on, is easy too — but be sure to use an equivalent mouthpiece design when you do. Likely cornet candidates could include young children (the cornet is smaller, sometimes lighter and offers a bit less blowing-resistance), brass/military bandsmen and jazz musicians many of whom like the tone and traditions of the short and long-model cornet. But for players over eleven, and all those interested in the mainstreams of music making (classical, dance band, many kinds of jazz or contemporary rock and pop music) the trumpet is the standard option. Choice made? Then next stop the music shop!

Your first instrument

Buying your first instrument is exciting. But it will cost quite a lot! So before committing yourself to a heavy bill right away, why not think about a cheaper alternative, for example:

(a) *Hiring a trumpet:* most good shops offer a hiring service. In return for a monthly rental you hire a brand-new instrument, and at the end of an agreed trial period — six months or a year — you make up your mind whether to return it, continue renting, or buy outright (your rental payments will be deducted from the cost price). Good idea, or you might like to try:

(b) *Banding:* your local Salvation Army or Silver band can provide not just an instrument but tuition and a band to play in as well. Schools often provide instruments too, but often only cheap or elderly ones — so think about a changeover after a year or so.

On the other hand, if you're like me, you may be quite sure that the best thing in the world is to have a brand new trumpet that's all your own. What a marvellous idea! So, once in the shopping centre find a music shop specialising in brass with a good range of stock and preferably without any sole-agency commitment to one manufacturer — this cuts down your choice. Ask the brass salesman if the shop has a commitment like this, and if he says 'yes' then treat his recommendations with just a little caution. A second opinion can help you with problems like these, and on this most important of first trips you'd be well advised to take a friendly local expert with you — perhaps the trumpet teacher you intend to study with. Most of them love spending money!

Once in the shop you'll probably be shown one or two super-cheap trumpets, often made in Russia or China. Be careful. Some superbuys are excellent value for money — others are bad bargains. You could start your playing career with a poor-toned out-of-tune instrument handicapped by sluggish valve action and dismally cheap lacquer finish which doesn't last a month. Once the novelty has worn off (with the lacquer) you'll be fighting your instrument at a time when — really — you need all the help and encouragement you can get. So if you *do* buy cheaply make sure good advice is at hand first. And if money is really a problem why not consider hiring or. . .

Second hand buying

A very good idea. Make sure your local expert is with you, or use the following checklist to be sure of a bargain:

(a) Is the trumpet made by a well-known manufacturer? And are they still in business? In any case find out where the nearest workshop or brass repair service is. You may need it sometime.

(b) Have a look at the diagram on p. 10 and make sure the trumpet has no vital parts missing!

(c) Is the trumpet dent-free? Make sure there are no big ones.

(d) Check that the mouthpiece is removable and that all four tuning slides will pull out by hand:-

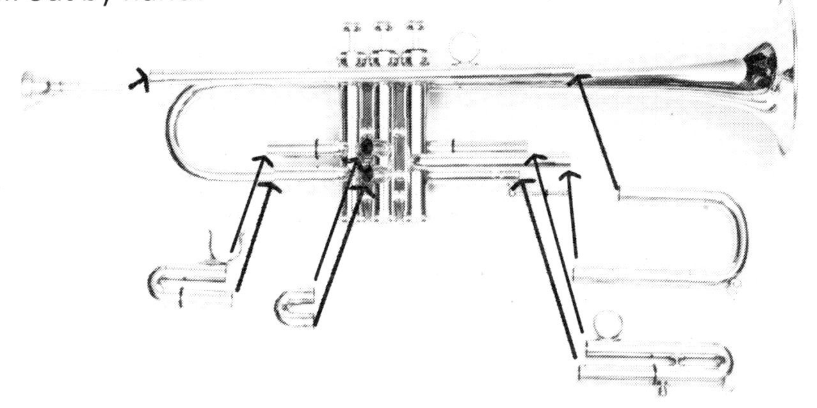

(e) Check that the spit valve(s) or more properly water key(s) work and have corks:-

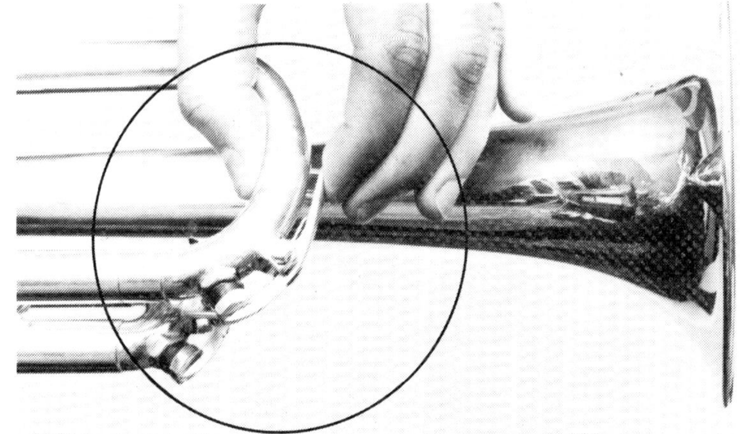

(f) Check that the trumpet has no leaks, and plays in tune (ask your expert). A do-it-yourself method of leak-checking is to blow cigarette smoke through the mouthpiece (any holes act as chimneys) but this is for adults only, and risky all round.

(g) Holding each valve top in turn try to move the valves gently from side to side. If there is lots of 'play' the valves are worn and the instrument may leak. Check that the valves move up and down freely, silently and reasonably easily:-

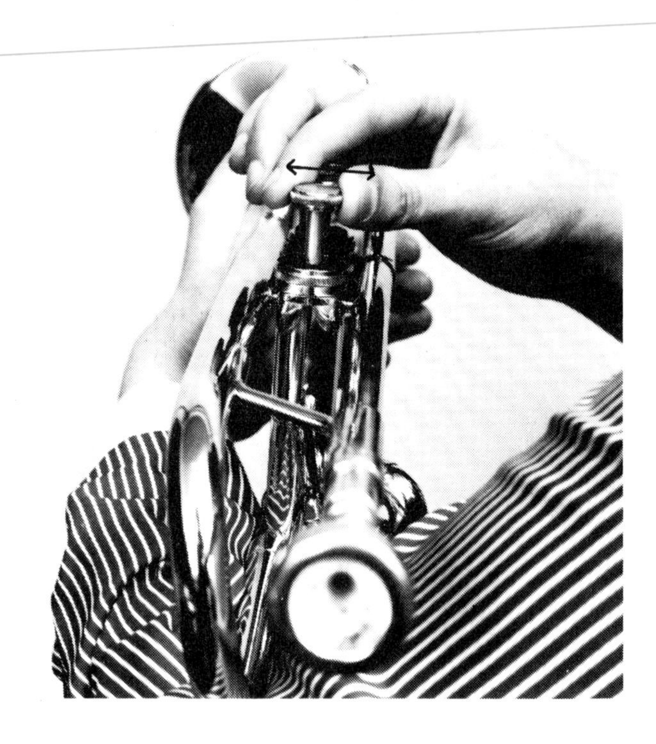

(h) Unscrew the valves one at a time and make sure the nickel-plated interiors are in good trim. (Don't worry about natural 'bulges' in the metal but beware of holes!) Then put the valves back **in the same order:-**

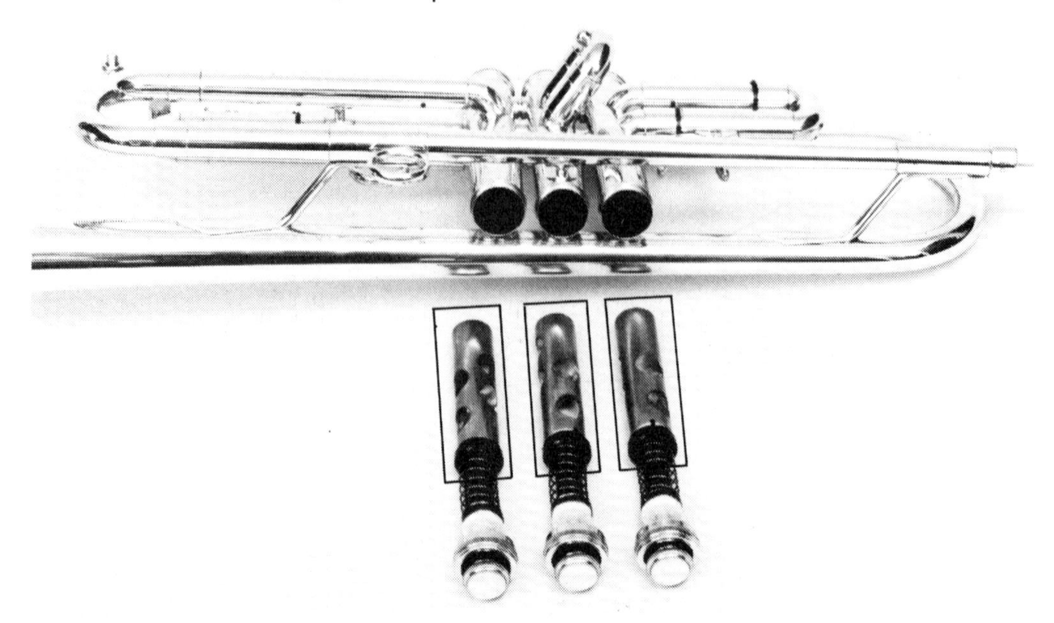

(i) Take out the middle-valve slide. Press down valve 2. Make sure that the slide apertures correspond exactly to the valve apertures.

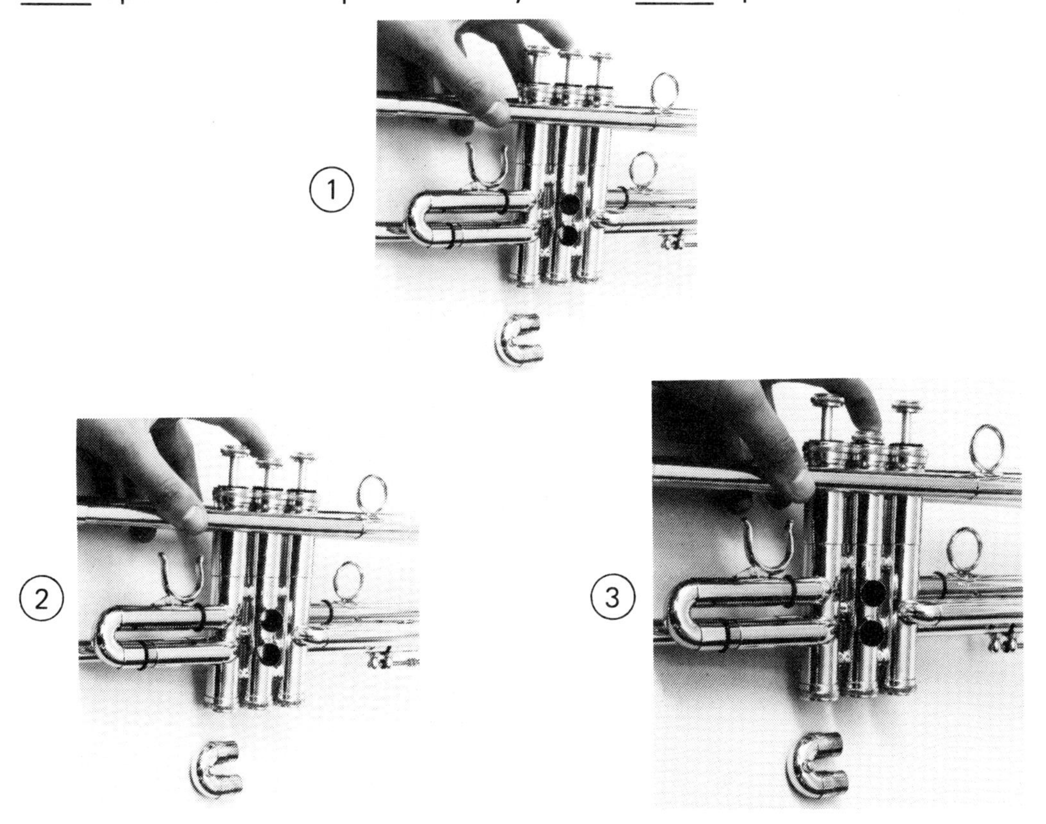

(j) Don't be afraid to (politely) ask the salesman how much the current list-price of your purchase would be if bought new — and ask him how *old* his bargain offer is.

If you have any doubts contact the manufacturer and quote the instrument's serial number — normally stamped on one of the valves.

(k) Finally, look your trumpet over. Does it look good — and does it please you? Good — then buy. How about 'on appro'?

Approval buying

Most stores will allow you a trial buying period for your new trumpet (seven to fourteen days is reasonable) if you give them a cheque for the full purchase cost. This is very good for double-checking the advisability of any new or secondhand purchase — and if you think again you'll get all your money back. Any other way, no.

And the mouthpiece?

Your mouthpiece is the vital link between you and the instrument. So do make sure:

(a) That the mouthpiece is a reputable make. This should ensure soundness of design and make it easy to replace if lost.

(b) That the mouthpiece rim is *not more than ¼ of an inch wide* **at most,** and the cup *not less than ¼ of an inch deep* **at least.** In other words a standard design, and suitable for learning on. Ask the salesman — or your teacher-friend — to make sure.

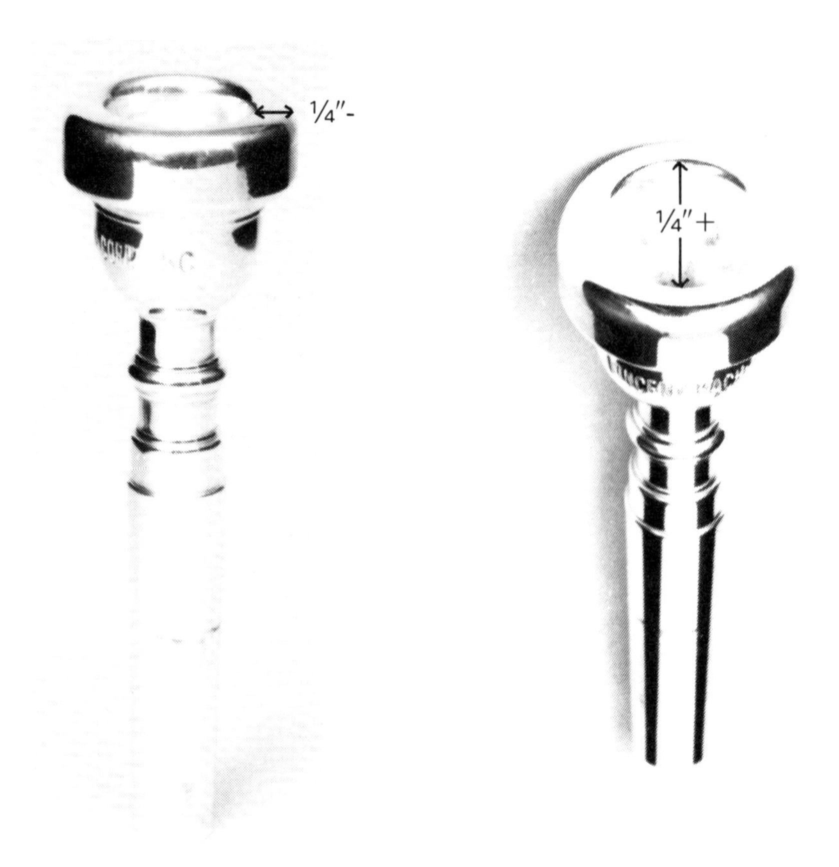

Selecting a case

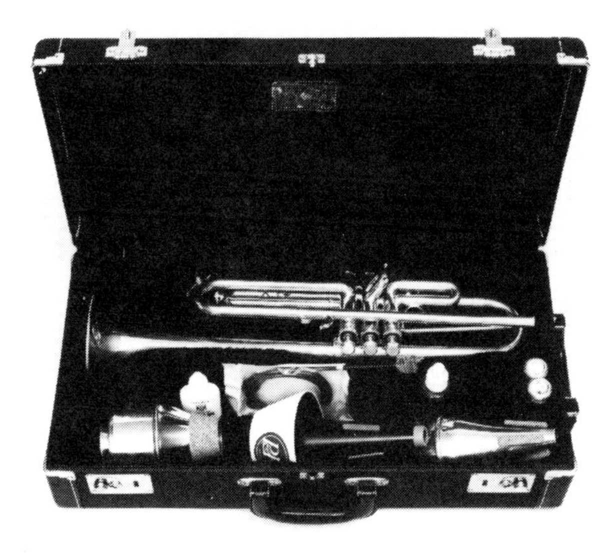

Your new trumpet should come with a case to match — but if not, do buy one right away. Hard cases are better — soft ones, though lighter and attractive looking, sure enough, can never protect your beautiful new instrument from dents. Check that the case is stout and lockable — and that there's a large compartment for mutes, cleaning cloths, and general accessories.

And finally mutes

Well, mutes are really a luxurious extra — at least to begin with. The trumpet should always be practised *open* — the noise level shouldn't be prohibitive, and it's most important in the early days (and later on too!) to listen carefully to your open tone; mutes can disguise faults. If noise is really a big problem, even with the windows closed, buy a Straight Mute which faithfully echoes your open tone and never distorts tuning as other mutes can.

Alternatively, try a piece of bathroom flannel elasticated at the edges over the bell, to take the edge off the sound

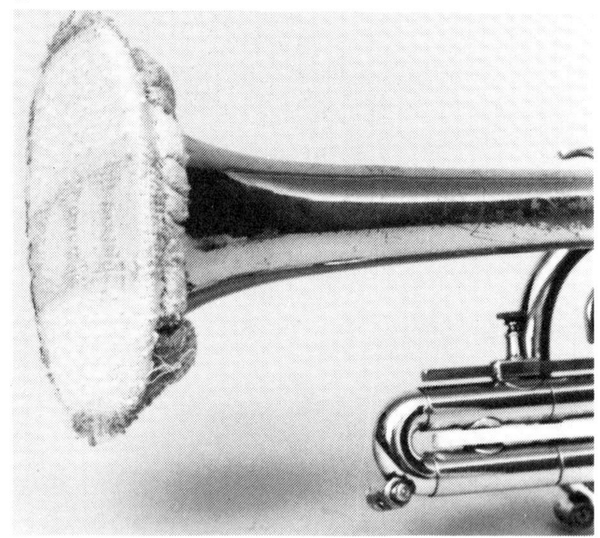

or — as a first reserve — a Practice Mute (one of the small ones) which cuts the sound of the trumpet dramatically.
You can buy Practice Mutes in any good brass shop and my only reservations are (A) that they disguise your open tone completely which is not a good idea, especially early on and (B) that the larger ones in particular may encourage you to blow too hard. However, your family might override these objections!

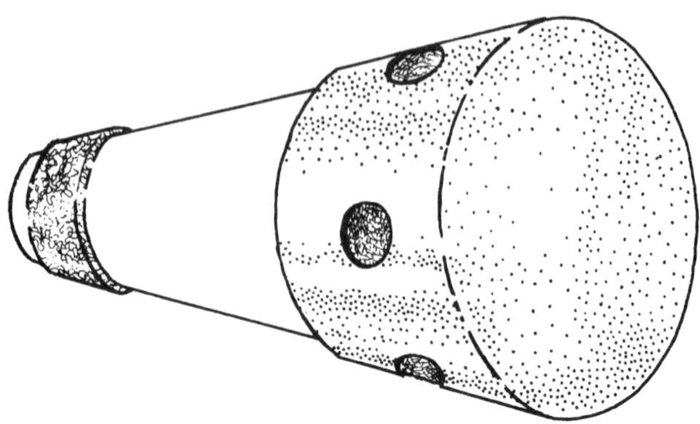

Buy other mutes when you are ready and always stick to standard makes. Fibre, metal and plastic mutes usually sound best (in that order); wooden mutes should be purchased with care.

How to look after the beast!

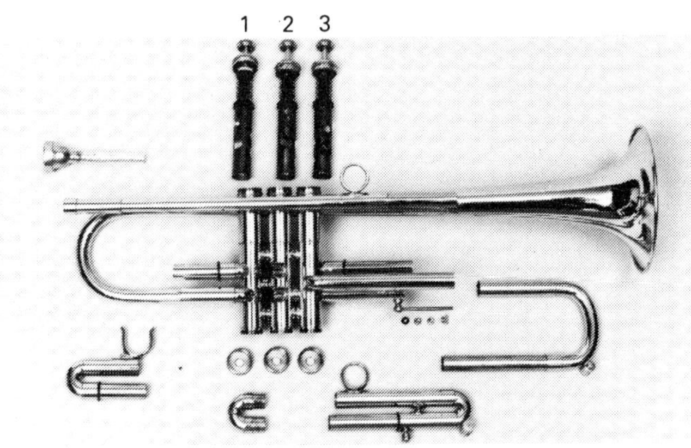

You'd think your brand new trumpet ought to run as smoothly as a brand new limousine. And just occasionally it may. But more often than not a trumpet new from the factory line needs running in too — just like a limousine! It'll probably be sluggish with oil and lubricant from the assembly plant — and an old instrument may just be clogged with the sands of time! So either way dismantle it carefully making sure valves 1, 2 and 3 don't get mixed up, (lay them out in order) and wash each part in hot soapy water. Flush the bell, tubes, shanks and slides similarly. Then wash everything again in clean hot water, without soap. You may need to do this two or three times before the trumpet is really clean. Then dry thoroughly outside and in — a 'non-shed' cloth hung on a knitting needle will dry inside the slides for you — and apply Vaseline (just a little) to the slides and a recommended valve oil to the valves.

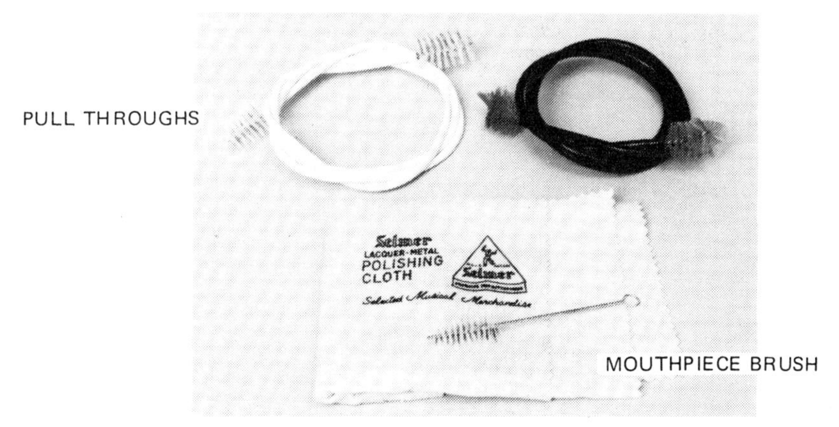

From then on, if you play regularly (of *course* you do!) wash the trumpet once a fortnight, using properly-designed trumpet and mouthpiece cleaners from the shop. (Buy these individually rather than in a kit — it's cheaper!) The first shank along to the main tuning slide is where most dirt will collect — so make that the centre of future operations.

Stuck?

If a slide (or the mouthpiece) becomes jammed take the trumpet back to the shop — or a repairer. Never try and do the job with pliers — brute force and good intentions usually end up in a steep repair bill. Boiling water applied to the offending area followed by a swift tug will occasionally do the trick but *do* be careful (nag, nag) and never force the issue.

For cleaning

Wipe the trumpet clean with a dry cloth after use.
Use a proper trumpet polish, or an impregnated cleaning cloth for shining up, and never use metal polish. *Ever!*
If you can find one, a lace-up valve sheath around the valves (try it on the trumpet before you buy it) is a luxurious idea:-

Simple Music Theory

Music for the trumpet is written down in notes like these:

on and between the five lines of the stave or staff.

At the start of trumpet music we find a treble clef like this 𝄞 and the stave is divided up by bar-lines (or bars as the Americans call them) into bars (or measures as the Americans call them).

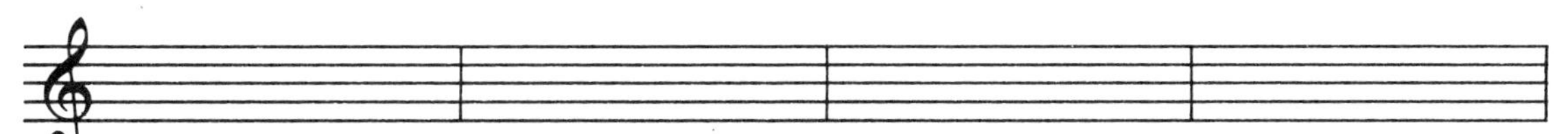

The notes with which we write (and pitch) the music are named after the first seven letters of the alphabet:

— and these notes vary in length according to what kind of notes they are:

a whole note or semibreve 𝅝 which is four beats long,

a half note or minim 𝅗𝅥 which is two beats long,

a quarter note or crotchet ♩ which is one beat long,

an eight note or quaver ♪ which is half a beat long,

a sixteenth note or semiquaver 𝅘𝅥𝅯 which is a quarter beat long.

This (♭) is called a Flat, and lowers any note by one step, or **semitone.**

This (♯) is called a Sharp, and raises any note by one step or **semitone.**

UNIT 2

Starting in – Holding the trumpet

Grip the valves of the trumpet in a good firm grip with the thumb and first three fingers of your left hand. The third finger should pass through the finger ring on the third valve slide (if there's a ring on it) and your little finger rests on or under the slide.

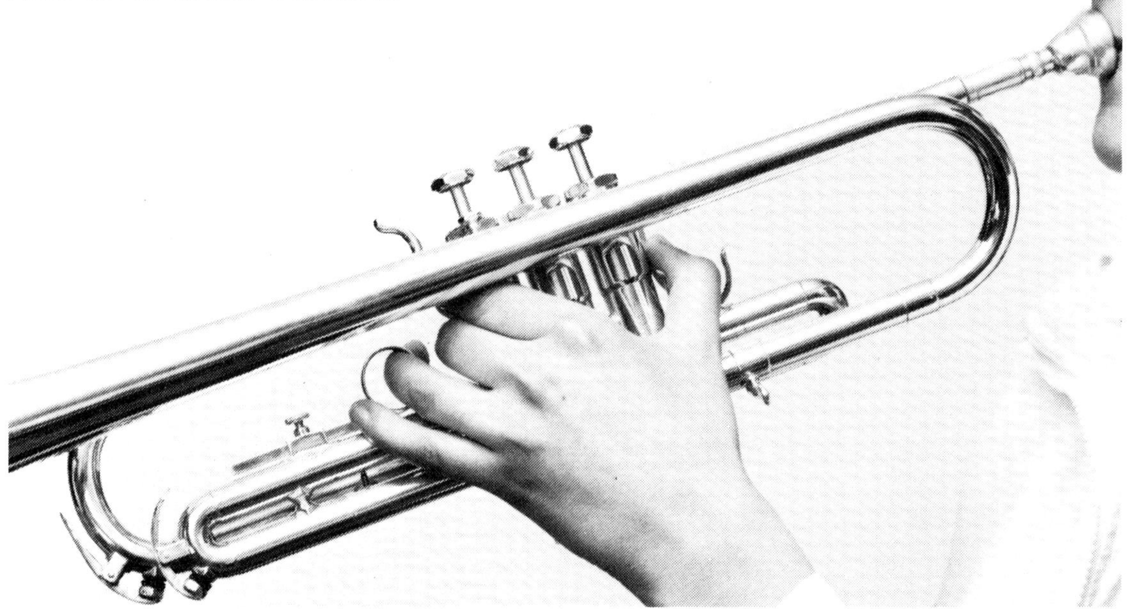

Now for your right hand. Tuck your thumb between the first and second valves and gently rest the tips of your first, second and third fingers on valve tops 1, 2 and 3. Your little finger passes through the hook or ring on the main shank (if there is one). Have a look at the picture, and there you are.

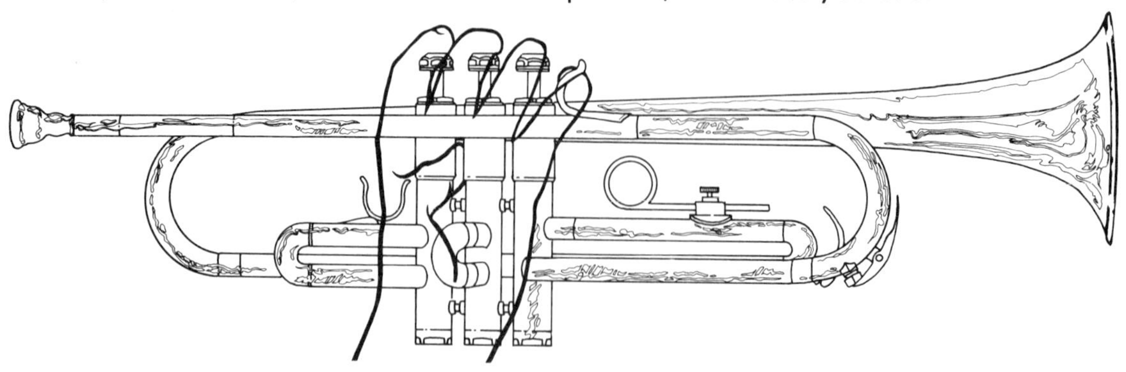

GOLDEN RULE 1

Always press the valves down with your fingertips — never with the thickness of your fingers. Playing on the thickness reduces speed and facility, increases pressure on your lips, and *looks* ugly.

Standing or sitting?

Standing

Right

Wrong

Sitting

Right

Wrong

It's always best to stand while practising. If you must sit, use a stool or hard backed chair and either way sit up straight with your shoulders down and back straight. That way, sitting or standing you'll be breathing properly and your diaphragm and muscles will have room to work (see the next chapter for some ideas on diaphragmatic breathing). Never practise seriously while you're relaxing in an armchair or stretched out on the sofa in what Stanley Holloway calls a 'somnolent post-ure'. All your breathing tackle is misplaced — not a good idea.

Getting ready to play

(a) Take out the trumpet mouthpiece and blow through it gently to warm up the metal.

(b) Now try *buzzing*. Purse your lips together and then pass air through them to produce (with luck) a buzzing noise. If this won't come, try and activate the sound by going through the motions of spitting a speck of tobacco from the end of your tongue. When you can produce the buzz confidently place the mouthpiece on your lips in a central position and repeat the exercise until you can buzz through the mouthpiece at will. Take your time! — this is a fundamental exercise that could take a week. But what a well-spent week!

(c) Now — a week later if necessary! — put the mouthpiece back in the trumpet, and set the instrument to your lips as centrally as is comfortably possible. Check that the mouthpiece rests — for a rough guide — 50% on the skin above the upper lip, and 50% on the lower. *Never* let the mouthpiece rest on the pink flesh of the lip itself. Have a look in a mirror to make sure.

RIGHT!

WRONG!

Now, holding the trumpet out straight and without pressing any valves down repeat the buzzing exercise through the trumpet and hang on to the sound!

When you can distinguish a proper note, it will probably be either 'C' or 'G'

For the time being concentrate on producing whichever note comes easiest. Find out which one it is by checking against a keyboard, tuning fork, pitch pipe or some other checkpoint remembering this rule.

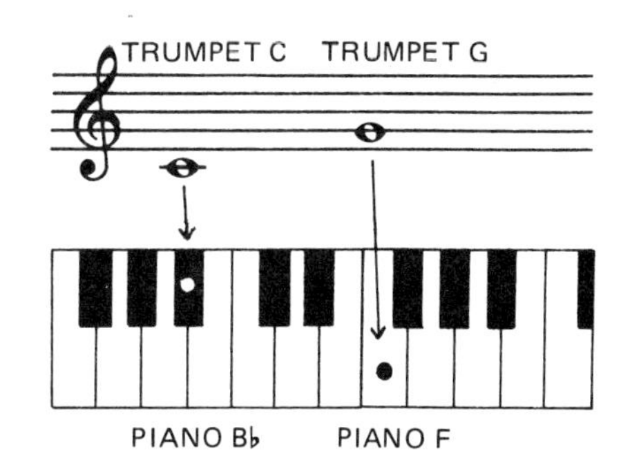

If the G is coming well, slacken the lip to produce C as well — a *lower* note. If C is coming well, then reverse the process — tighten the lip muscles (by pulling away from the mouthpiece) and try to find G — a higher note.

When you have located both notes you can begin your first practice routine.

Practice routine

(a). Isolate G and C in your mind — how they *feel* to play, and where they are on the stave.

(b). Practise playing both to a slow count of three, then six.

(c). Get used to listening to yourself. Is the note pleasing to your ear? If not, regulate it by adjusting your lip and breathing until a clear regular uninterrupted sound comes.

If this is difficult on G then concentrate on low C for the time being. Work conscientiously on these notes for a week or so (no more than a minute at a time followed by a minute's rest, ten-minutes maximum) until they sound reasonable.

Tonguing

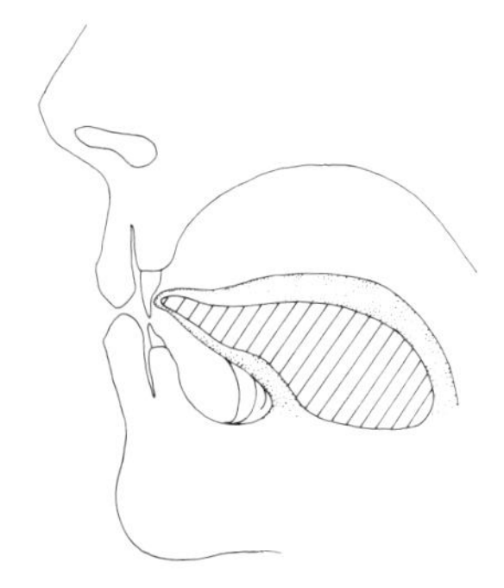

This process ensures clear note production and is standard trumpet practice.
Try saying 'ta' (some trumpeters prefer 'da'. So try both!) Notice how your tongue strikes the back of the top teeth (nowhere else) and quickly withdraws. This is just the way to tongue a note.

Now try playing a C or G starting it off with a 'ta' or 'da'. This should help you to produce the note quickly, cleanly and with a good tone. Make sure the sound is not *too* clipped however — it should still sound musical and retain its full length.

GOLDEN RULE 2

Listen to these first exercises. Try to make sure every note stays in tune, and begins and ends cleanly. Once you've started to listen critically to the way you play, cultivate the habit — and always be your own sternest critic! Remember Louis Armstrong's own 'golden rule' — 'If it *sounds* good, it very probably *is* good!'

Now here are some simple exercises. Tongue each note 'ta' or 'da'.

Tunes to play

Now for two simple tunes! Think and Count!

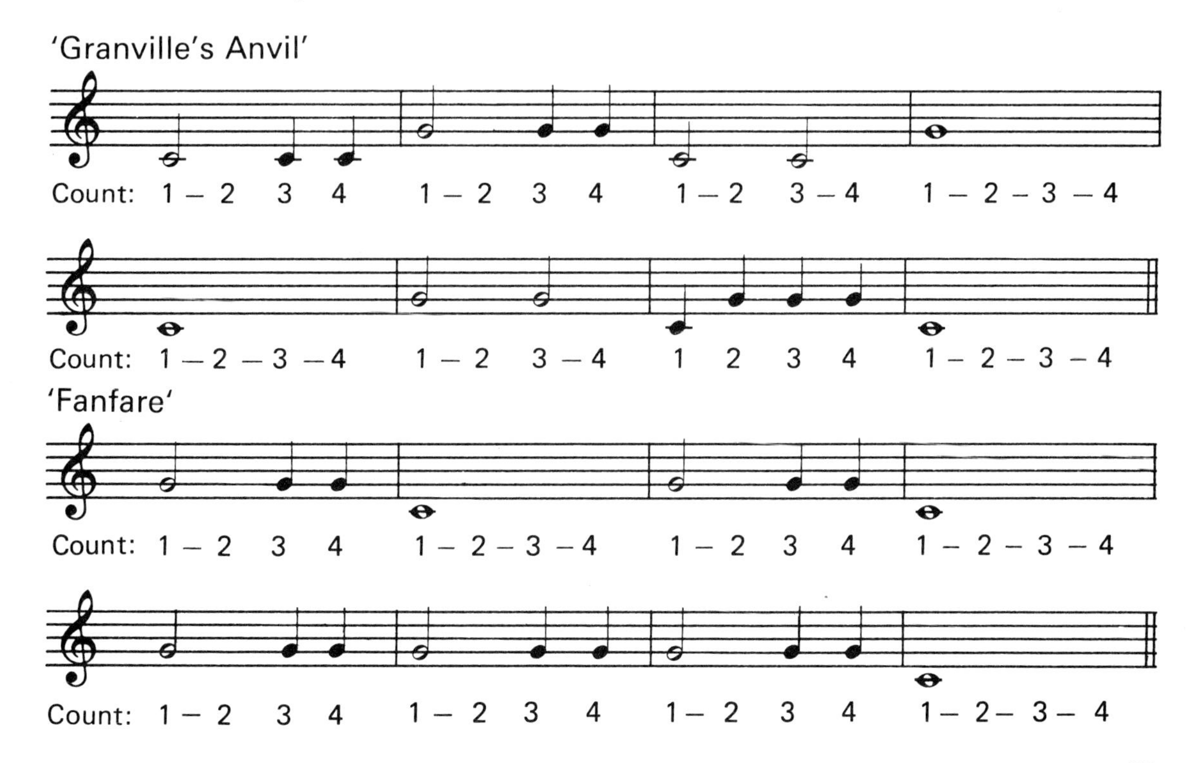

UNIT 3

Now, about breathing — or you and your diaphragm

In recent years more and more brass and woodwind players have taken up diaphragmatic breathing — a way of breathing more deeply and so playing even better than before!

The idea of even slightly adjusting how you breathe might sound alarming, paramedical and even risky. To begin with, it did to me. 'After all' I thought . . . 'I play the trumpet for fun, but I breathe for a living!' There was no need to worry. Diaphragmatic breathing — as I quickly found out — was really just a scientific name for deep breathing — and that has a long medical pedigree. *You* could be breathing from the diaphragm automatically but if not only a slight adjustment is necessary to the method that's happily carried you through so far!

Take a look at a newborn baby. See the way baby breathes? The *stomach* rises and falls steadily and naturally as breath is drawn in and out — because our young demonstrator is breathing automatically from the *diaphragm*. Which suggests that was what nature intended all along. Later on in life social influences encourage us to do it the wrong way. "Chest out — stomach in!" encourages the eurythmics instructor as he turns us into barrel-chested he-men or bosomy lovelies. "Throw your chest out" he emphasises, compounding the felony. The trouble is that inflating just the *chest* with air leaves the larger, lower half of our lungs without any work to do. "Shallow breathing never gives the blood time to absorb what little oxygen has been taken in" warns Michael Volin ('Growing up with Yoga' Pelham Books, 1967) "— and when we exhale we leave a residue of stale air in the lungs" ("Not enough to kill us!" he adds encouragingly). This is where diaphragmatic breathing comes in. When we take a really deep breath the diaphragm — a long flat muscle situated at the bottom of the lungs descends, the ribs rise, and the air-filled lungs expand downwards — and outwards — under the ribs.

Try a simple exercise to prove the point:

(a) Locking your thumbs around the back of your lungs, touch your fingertips across your stomach.

(b) Now slowly breathe in. Let your stomach push forward so that your fingers are pushed apart. Hold the air in.

(c) Breathe out, drawing in your stomach as air is exhaled. Good!

(d) Now *after a rest* do the same exercise again, breathing in to a count of eight seconds. Try to push the lower stomach and kidney area outwards as the air inflates the lower lungs. Then when the bottom lungs are full gulp in air through your *mouth* to inflate the upper chest last of all. Hold the air in for as long as possible and then slowly — slowly — exhale. No . . . *slower!*

Now think about that final exhalation. Why should it be slow? Because if the air is blown out in a windy gasp the exercise is pointless — that air is intended for your trumpet mouthpiece. So make sure you breathe out slowly — to a count of about eight seconds — and see that the flow of air is controlled by you and your mighty diaphragm. Then when your lungs are comfortably empty continue pushing out, out, out (phew!) and wait for a couple of seconds before slowly inhaling again.

There! That's full diaphragmatic breathing. The first few times you may find yourself turning a pretty pink, or coughing. But that's only because — perhaps for years — you haven't been breathing as deeply as you can, or probably should, and the lower half of your lungs became lazy. Just now you took a *really* deep breath — and your body reacted naturally to a vigorous and healthy new exercise. Like any good body it'll soon tone up and shape up.

To begin breathing more fully takes time of course. It can never come naturally right away. So try to practise in spare moments — walking to work, in the office, or best of all — in front of a mirror for two minutes each morning. Gradually you'll find that diaphragmatic breathing becomes as easy as . . . well, breathing.

This principle is of the greatest value in trumpet playing. A strong column of air is vital at all times — and problems which occasionally bother advanced players often stem from insufficient or incorrect breathing. Now that you're "thinking diaphragm" of course you'll never have to worry about *that*.

GOLDEN RULE 3

(a short one this time!)

Think diaphragm!

UNIT 4

Playing the notes in between C & G

In Unit 2 we played open notes G and C.

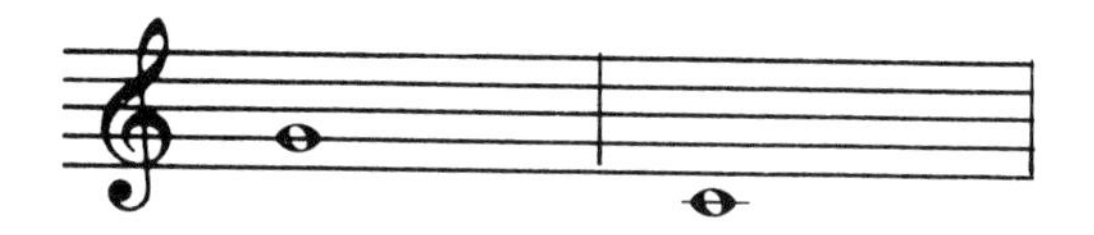

Now buzz the lip to warm up (see p. 28) and play the notes in between.
Slacken the lip gradually as you go down . . .

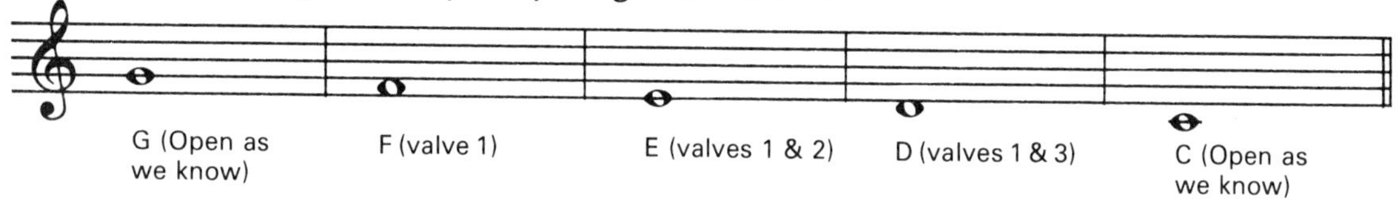

Then tighten the lip gradually as you go up again . . .

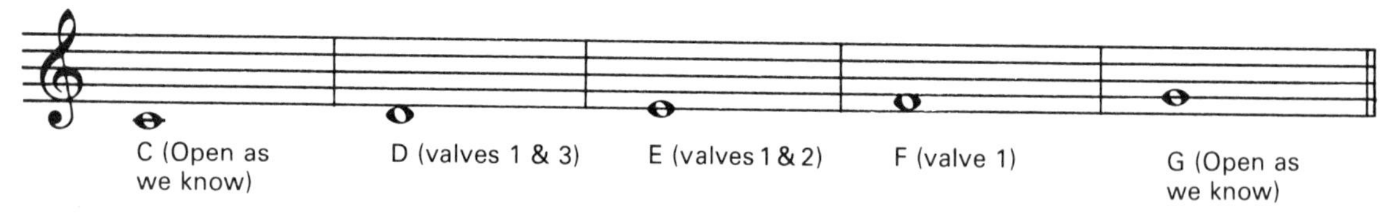

Long notes: A very important exercise

A well played long note looks (and sounds) like this:

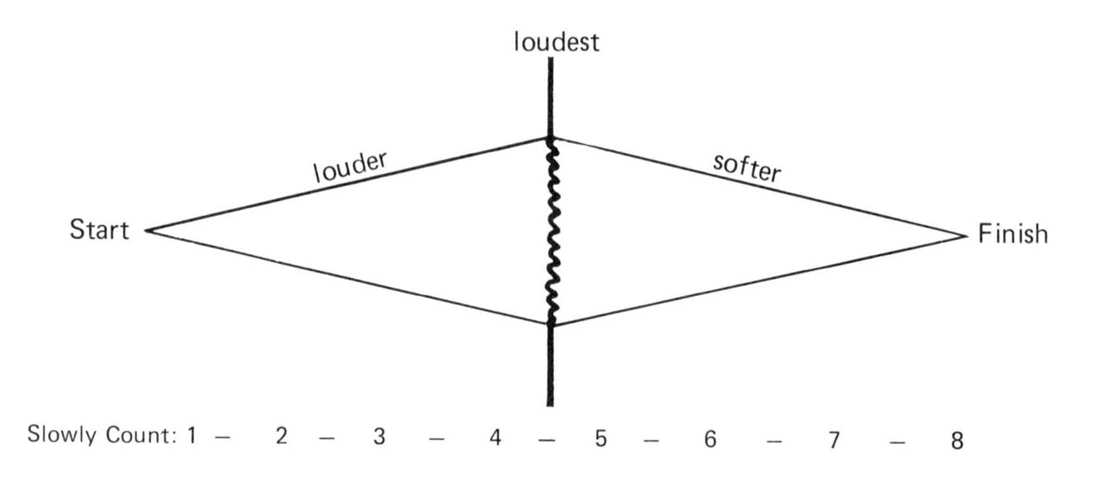

To play a long note like this remember the golden rule:

GOLDEN RULE 4

Long Notes

Fix a slow count of 8 in your mind — pitch your note ('ta' or 'da') at a whisper — slowly increase the airflow and volume 1,2,3 — louder — to the loudest point at 4 (halfway) — then gently softer again 5 — and softer 6 — until by 7 and 8 the note whispers to a stop —

And rest.

To a count of approximately eight seconds try this with all new notes.

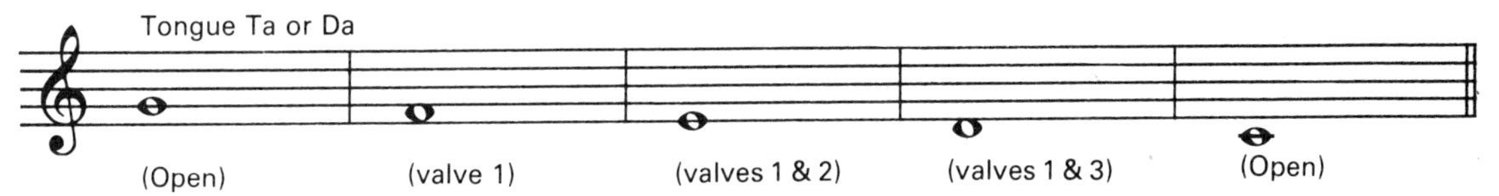

'Elpful do's and don'ts

(a) Make sure the note starts surely, as soon as you tongue it. Don't cheat — if there's a delay, rest and try again.

(b) Make sure the *crescendo* (loud lead up) is gradual, controlled, and sounds *good.*

(c) Make sure that at their loudest the notes are still controlled — no louder than comfortable. Never overblow or roll your lower lip out for the sake of volume — you'll hear the bad results all too clearly.

(d) As the note gets softer make sure that tone and sound remain good, and well supported by air. At the very end make sure the note stops when *you* want it to — not when **it** wants to.

And now congratulations! Learn this exercise thoroughly, practise it for a couple of minutes a day, and one fundamental key to good trumpet playing is yours for keeps! Now on to the exercises . . .

Play long notes for now, no longer than you can comfortably manage. Don't strain!
Make sure the notes are 'centred' and in tune.

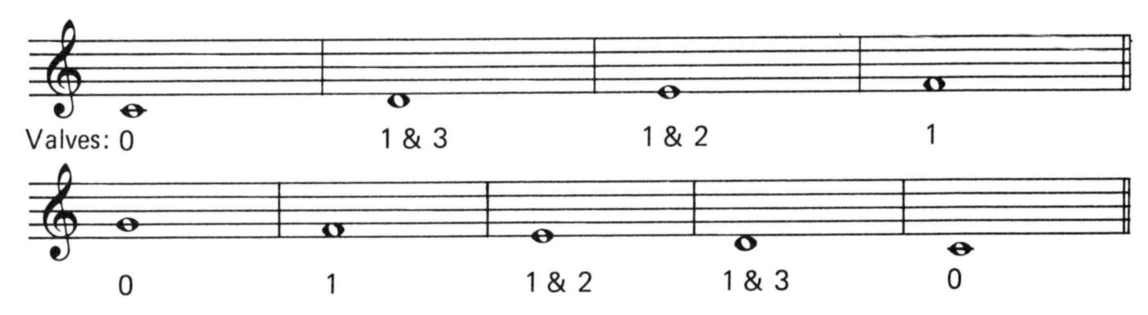

Now play the exercises below slowly and carefully. Tongue each note 'ta' or 'da'. Look back to p.35 if you have to.

7
Brightly and Steadily
8
Tunes to play
'Polka'
Brightly and steadily
'Anthem'
Slowly with dignity

'Go Tell Aunt Rhody'
LOUDER
'Largo' New World Symphony (Dvorak)
'Jingle Bells'

UNIT 5 (not before week 4)
Trying out some new notes

When you know how to play the previous notes you can try out these new ones. Warm up thoroughly first with buzzing and a run through the previous exercises. Here are the new notes:

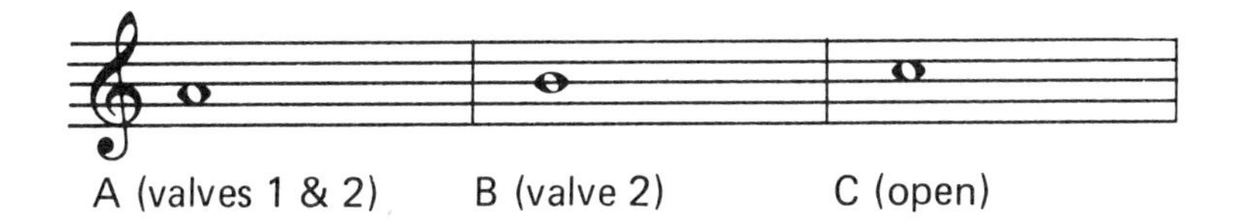

Now check. Do the new notes feel:

(a) Unfamiliar but comfortable?

(b) Unfamiliar but reasonably comfortable?

(c) A strain to play without lots of effort and pressure?

If the answer is (a) or (b) then you should be able to work through Units 6 to 8 quite quickly and easily. If the answer is (c) then backtrack. Replay A and B and find out at which note the strain starts to feel unreasonable. And stop there for the time being. Another golden rule for all trumpeters:

GOLDEN RULE 5

Take your time

There's plenty! And don't feel discouraged if now and then you have to nurse your developing lip along. Forming an embouchure is a delicate business and good groundwork laid at its own pace is essential.

Now, *when you're ready,* on we go to Unit Six.

UNIT 6 Note A

Warm up thoroughly and try it.

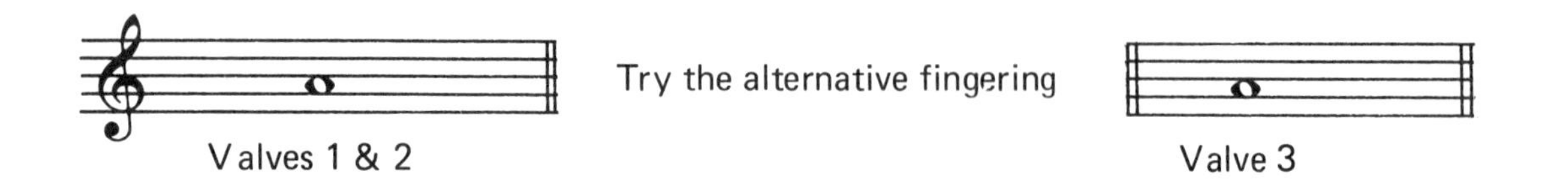

Now if all is well try these exercises. Take frequent rests and don't force things.

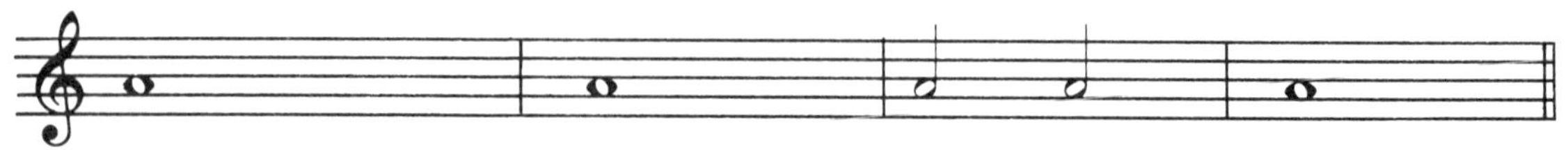
Long note as practised

When the note sounds centred, in-tune and pleasing to your ear try the exercises.

Rests

When a composer wants silence instead of music he writes 'rests' instead of notes. We count them in just the same way. So:

A wholenote (semibreve) rest is four beats long and looks like this:

Now play and count this exercise:

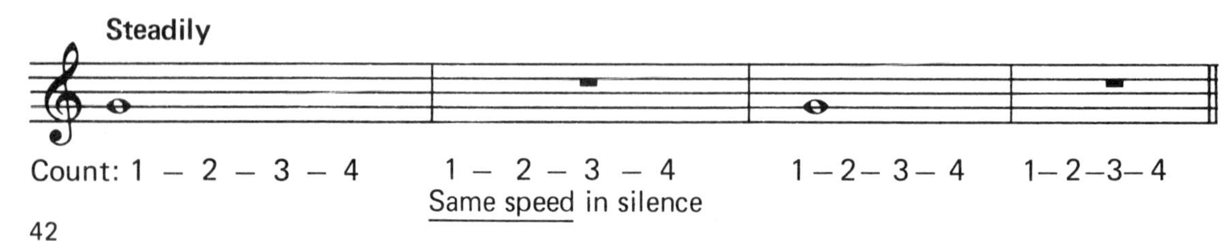

Good! Now a half-note (or minim) rest, which is two beats long, and looks like this:

(My way to remember the difference is that the wholenote (or semibreve) with *four* beats is strong enough to *hang* on the line; the half-note (or minim) with only two, is only strong enough to *sit* on it!)

Now play and count the exercise.

*And finally the quarter note or crotchet rest, just one beat, which looks like this 𝄽 (or occasionally this 𝄾). Play and count:

Now work out this one:

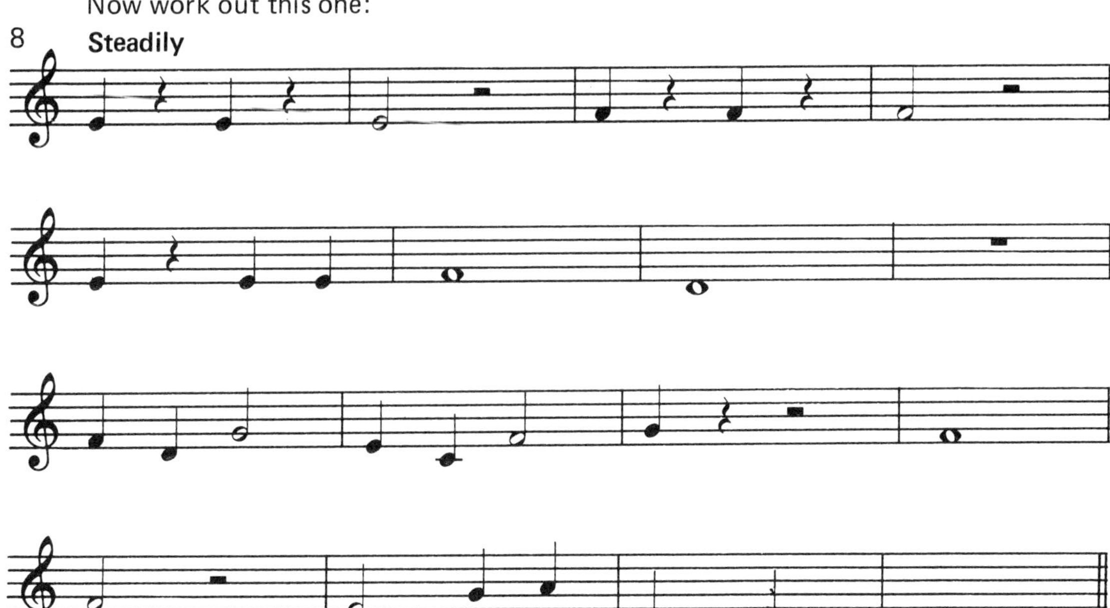

Good!

*Already briefly referred to on page 39.

GOLDEN RULE 6

When counting rests — and beats — set a regular rhythm in your mind to begin with, and *keep it there* while playing. Resist the temptation to rush ahead, or shorten notes and rest periods, and if necessary use a metronome to make sure you're not speeding, or cutting the value of notes or rests. This will help you to develop a good sense of *time* — very important.

New note low B

Play down to it from Open C.

Then a long note (remember the long note rule), and practise the note with rest periods until it sounds clear. Then play this:

9

Take your time. Low notes are difficult. Then play these exercises.

10

Eighth notes, or Quavers

Quavers are half the value of a crotchet in length. So there are eight to a bar of 4/4 time — which is why quavers are often called eighth-notes, especially in America.

You write them down like this.

or sometimes bracketed together like this or this

and the quaver rest looks like this .

To count quavers use another simple trick.

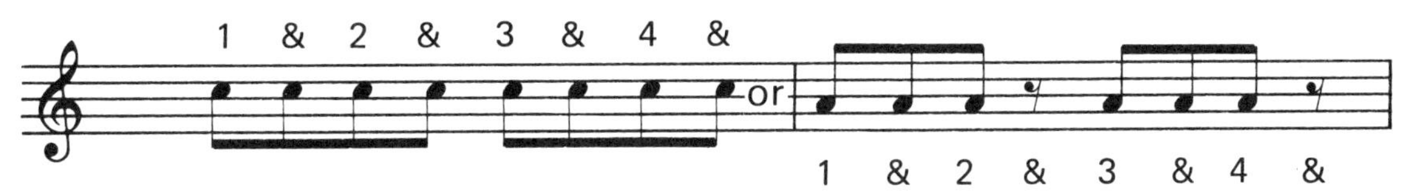

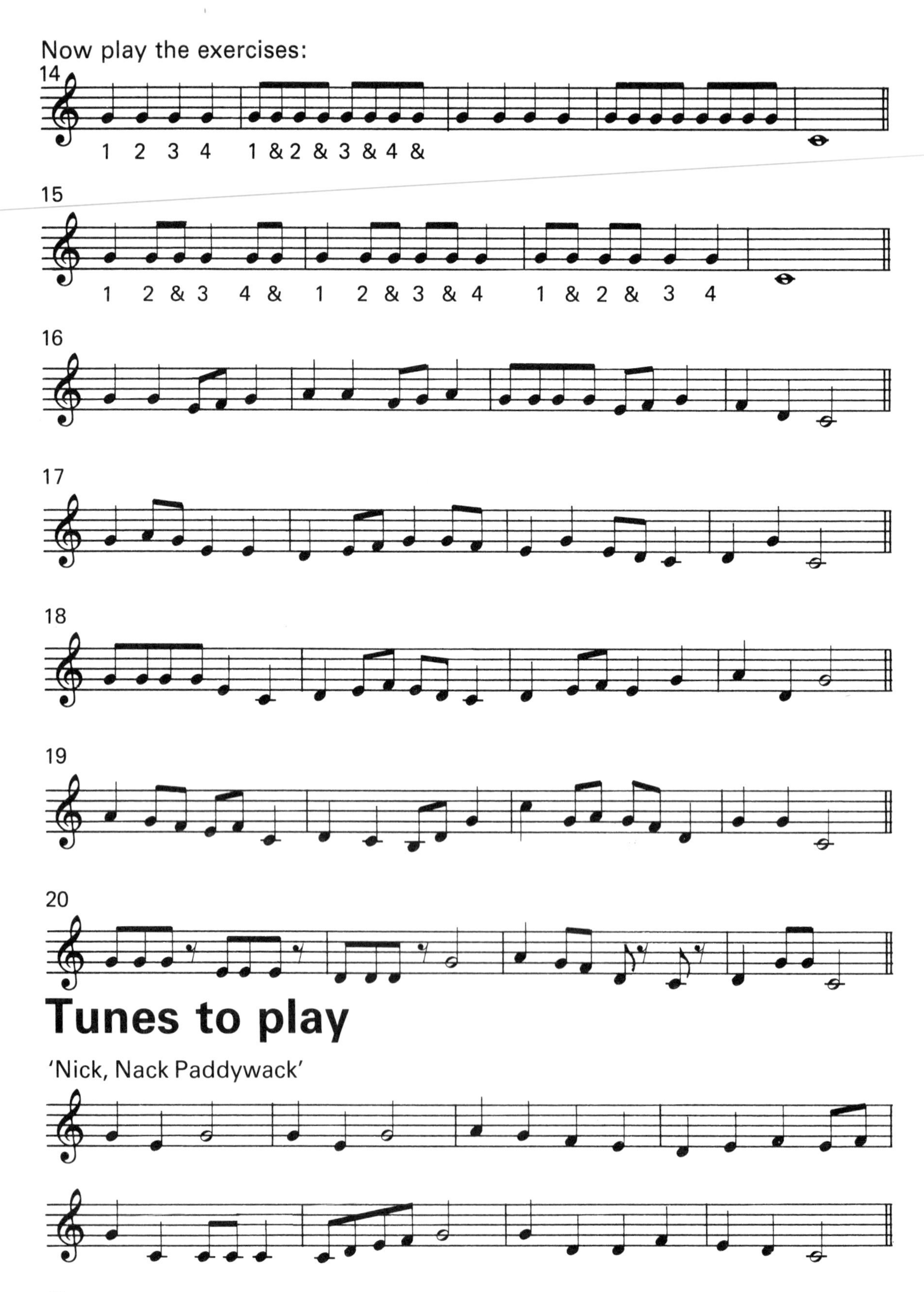
Now play the exercises:
14
1 2 3 4 1 & 2 & 3 & 4 &
15
1 2 & 3 4 & 1 2 & 3 & 4 1 & 2 & 3 4
16
17
18
19
20
Tunes to play
'Nick, Nack Paddywack'

'Old MacDonald Had A Farm'
Think! (2 3)
Think
'Frère Jacques'
— and 2 more favourite tunes to play! —
'Twinkle, Twinkle, Little Star'
'Michael, Row The Boat Ashore'
(1 — 2) 3 4

GOLDEN RULE 7

Practice

Like all good things it should be done little and often. In the early playing days, too much practice can slow up the good progress we're making. Try to play for ten minutes in the morning while your body and mind are still wide awake, fresh and alert. Then ten minutes more in the evening if you have time. And during those ten minute stints rest frequently — your newly developing embouchure is sensitive and straining or bruising its muscles in the cause of hard work is counter productive. Think how a sprinter slowly trains his muscles — and be like him!

If you lip starts to tire, spend a couple of minutes right away from the trumpet. Make a cup of tea, or watch TV, or wander around the garden. You'll come back physically and mentally refreshed.

UNIT 7 Note B

Warm up thoroughly and try it.

Valve 2

Now, if all is well, try these exercises. Don't force the notes and rest regularly.

Now try some more exercises.

2
3

Flats and sharps

The flat (♭) placed before any note lowers it by one half-tone (semitone).

(a) Try playing these examples and listen for the difference.

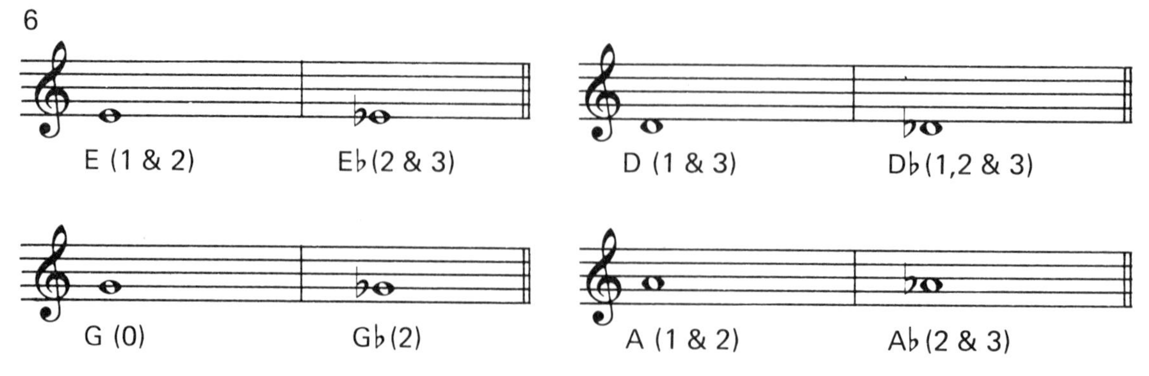

(b) The sharp (#) placed before any note raises it by one half-tone (semitone).

Now have a look at Eb in exercise 6, and D# in exercise 7. Notice anything? Here they are together:

2 & 3 2 & 3

Yes, they're the same note. Any note with two names (e.g. Eb or D#) is known as *enharmonic*. Whether we call the note Eb or D# depends on whether the key is a *sharp* or *flat* key, and this we know by looking to see if sharps or flats appear in the *key signature.*

The key signature

Every key apart from C contains automatically sharpened or flattened notes. To remind us which ones they are a **key signature** appears at the start of the music. For example, the key of G has one sharp, and its key signature looks like this:

Every time an F is written it will be automatically sharpened accordingly. The key of A has three sharps and its key signature looks like this:

Every time the F, C, and G are played they will be sharpened automatically.
Here are all the key signatures for reference:

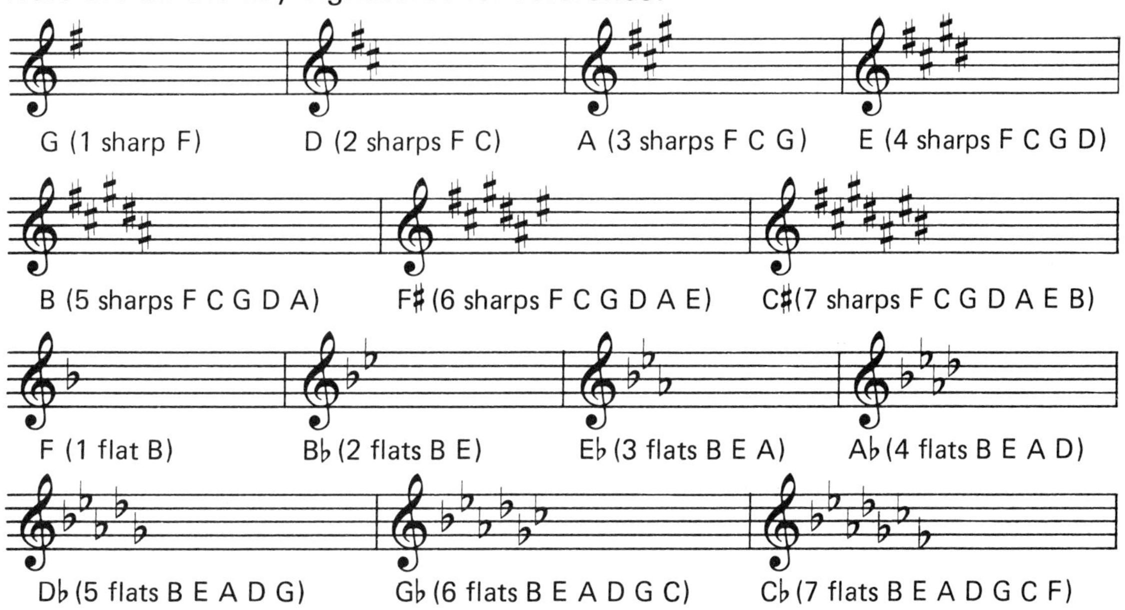

An easy way to remember all these is the 'Foxy Charlie' routine.

For sharp keys remember this sentence:

'FOXY CHARLIE GOES DOWN AND ENDS BOTHER'

To find the key with *one* sharp read the *one* word.

'FOXY'

Its first letter = the seventh note of the key concerned.

So the key with one sharp (F) is *G*!

To find the key with *two* sharps read along *two* words.

'FOXY CHARLIE'

The first letter of the last word = the seventh note of the key concerned.

So the key with two sharps (F and C) is *D*!

To find the key with *three* sharps read along *three* words.

'FOXY CHARLIE GOES'

The first letter of the last word = the seventh note of the key concerned.

So the key with three sharps (F, C and G) is *A*! And so on!

For flat keys read the sentence backwards!

'BOTHER ENDS AND DOWN GOES CHARLIE FOXY'

For the key with *one* flat read the one word.

'BOTHER'

Its first letter = the fourth note of the key concerned.

So the key with one flat = B + 4 = *F*!

For the key with *two* flats read *two* words.

'BOTHER ENDS'

The first letter of the last word = the fourth note of the key concerned.

So the key with two flats = E + 4 = Bb.

And so on. Q.E.D.

UNIT 8 Low Bb

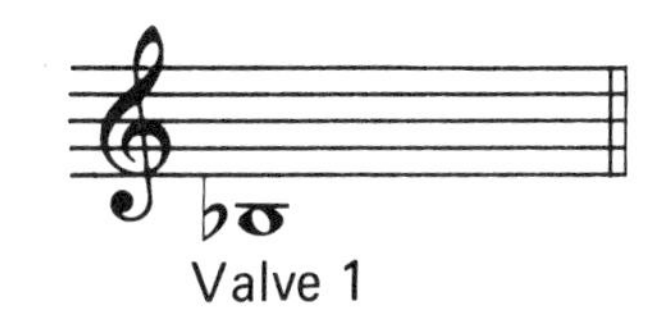

To play this note relax the lip and keep the throat open. Work down from low C in semitones to 'feel' the note correctly.

What key signature is this? Identify it – and now some more exercises:

Now something else to think about! Heavens!

*This note is B♮ (natural): see p. 87.

Time signatures

You find the time signature at the start of a piece of music. It's there to fix the number of beats in each bar and to let you know what *kind* of beats they are.

So:

4/4 = four crotchet beats to the bar (also written C).

3/4 = three crotchet beats to the bar.

2/4 = two crotchet beats to the bar.

5/4 = five crotchet beats to the bar.

6/8 = six quaver beats to the bar.

The C will also be found in some music written with a bar through it like this ₵. This usually indicates 2/4 time written as 4/4 for ease of reading. See the following examples.

2/4 = ₵

Look at the examples below, and see if you can work out the time signatures. See page 55 for the answers.

Answers to Examples 1 - 5 Page 54.

1. $\frac{4}{4}$ 2. $\frac{3}{4}$ 3. $\frac{2}{4}$ 4. $\frac{5}{4}$ 5. $\frac{6}{8}$

GOLDEN RULE 8

When you are faced with a passage of unfamiliar music to play look *first* at the *time signature* and the *key signature*. Fix the information they supply clearly in your mind before looking along to the notes. Forewarned is forearmed!

Tunes to play

'Down by the Riverside'

'Goodnight Ladies'
A dotted minim.
Count 3 beats.
1–2–3
(1 2 3)
1-2-3
1–2–3
(1 2 3)
1–2–3
1–2–3
(1 2) 3
1–2–3
(1 2 3)
'Yankee Doodle'
— And try this one again, in a new key,
(open)
(1— 2)
What's the key?
And what's the tune? Quite right!

UNIT 9 Note C

Warm up thoroughly, as usual with buzzing and a look at previous exercises, and try it.

OPEN

Then a long note, using our approved method,

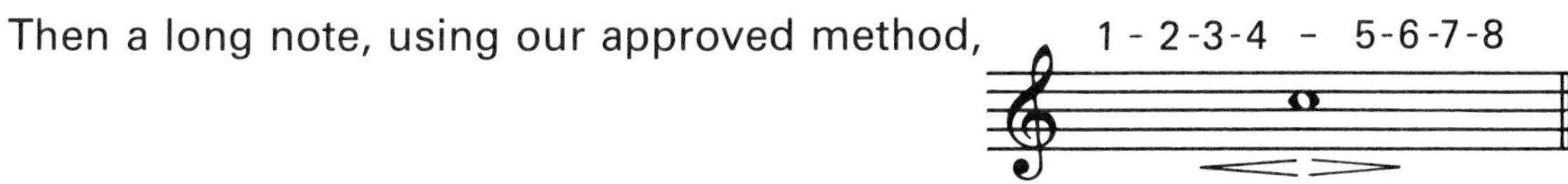

and then, if all is comfortable, try these exercises.

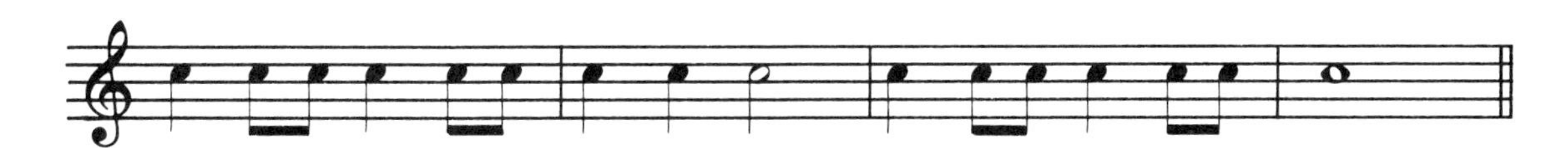

Now we can play the full scale of C.

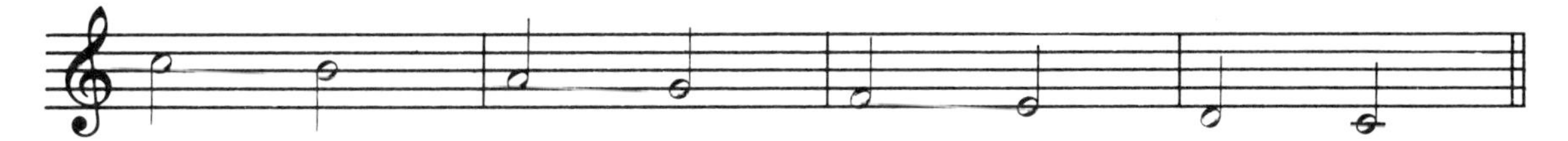

Some exercises:

1

5/6/9
2
3
Think!
4

5
CAREFUL!
6
7
8

Chromatic scales

Now we can look at the *chromatic* scale of C. A chromatic scale is a scale in which all twelve notes within the octave are played. So the chromatic scale of C looks like this:

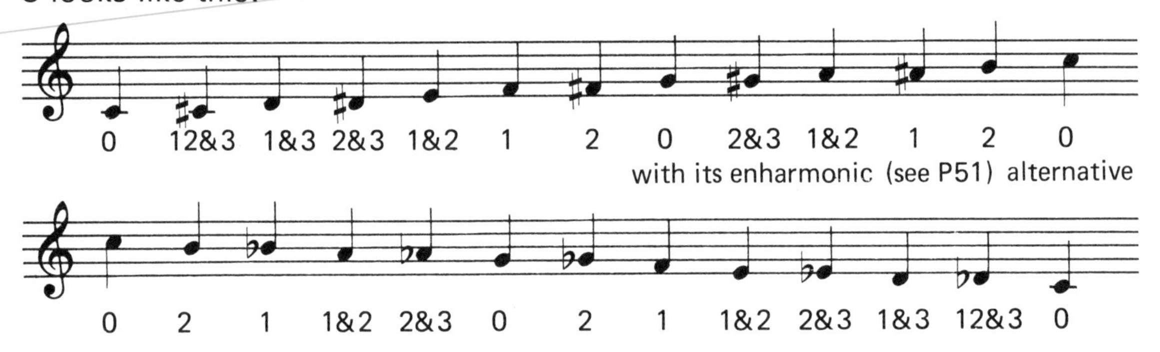

(a) Play up and down the chromatic scale carefully getting used to the fingering and watching the notation as you go.

(b) By regular practice, quicken the pace gradually, making sure every note is clearly played (press the valves down firmly — with the tips of your fingers, remember!)

The chromatic scale should become part of your daily practice. Try 'blind' practice too — ask a friend to call out notes at random from the scale and see how quickly you can play them back to him!

GOLDEN RULE 9

Make sure you know the fingering (and enharmonic alternate name!) for every note in the chromatic scale — as well as you know your ABC!

Ties and dots

When you see two of the same notes joined together by a curved line like this

— the notes are said to be 'tied' and played as a single note, to their collective length. Have a look at these tied notes and play them, counting carefully!

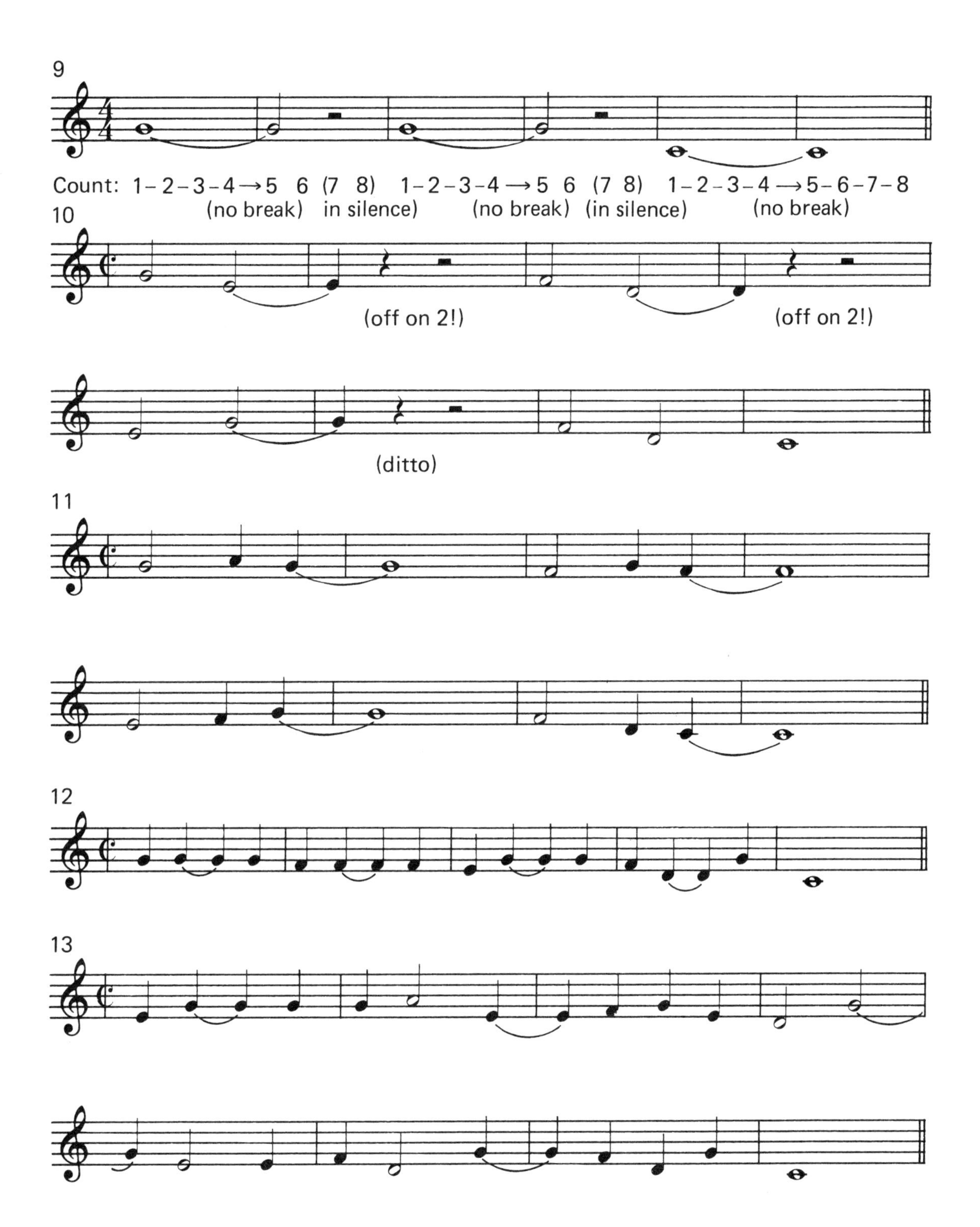
9
Count: 1–2–3–4→5 6 (7 8) 1–2–3–4→5 6 (7 8) 1–2–3–4→5–6–7–8
(no break) in silence) (no break) (in silence) (no break)
10
(off on 2!)
(off on 2!)
(ditto)
11
12
13

Another way to lengthen a note (or rest) is to use a *dot.* Placing a dot after a note increases its length by one-half its own value.

Look at and play these exercises.

GOLDEN RULE 10

Take it easy! —

all the way through our halfway exercises! Remember *all* the points so far.

19
20
FULL NOTE VALUES, BREATHE!
21

22
23

24
Play the next two cleanly!
25

26/6/95
26
Play very slowly and carefully!
27
Tunes to play:
'Sur Le Pont D'Avignon'
'Bobby Shaftoe'

'Beautiful Dreamer'
'Frankie and Johnny'
Breathe!

'Jaunty'
'Tristesse'
'Polka'
'Sad Waltz'

'Finaglin'

UNIT 10 New Note D

A new note D. Warm up with buzzing and a run through previous exercises moving up to higher notes gradually. Then try D.

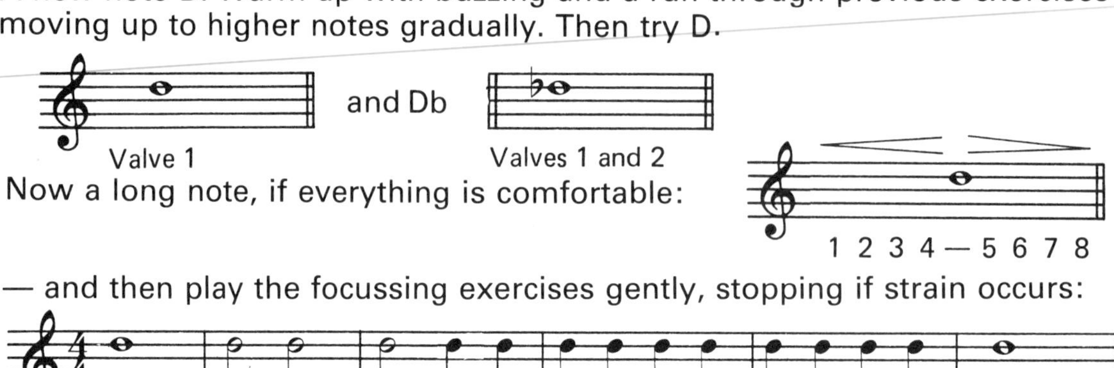

Now a long note, if everything is comfortable:

— and then play the focussing exercises gently, stopping if strain occurs:

The scale of D

The scale of D has two sharps: F and C as we know!

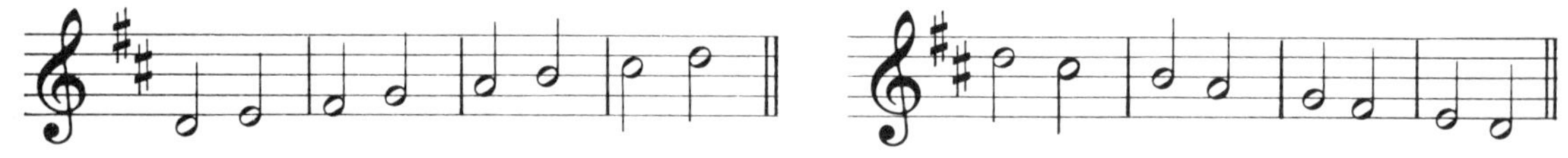

When you can play the scale try the exercises below.

Lip slurring and flexibility exercises.

'Flexibilities' are a very important exercise for the student. The basic idea is to play a series of simple and/or tricky intervals purely on the lip muscles — completely without help from the tongue, and often the slight difference in playing pressure caused by pressing valves down. Practising the exercises regularly will do a tremendous amount to strengthen your lip, and increase its flexibility in performance.

Now try playing the following slowly in one breath, without tonguing:

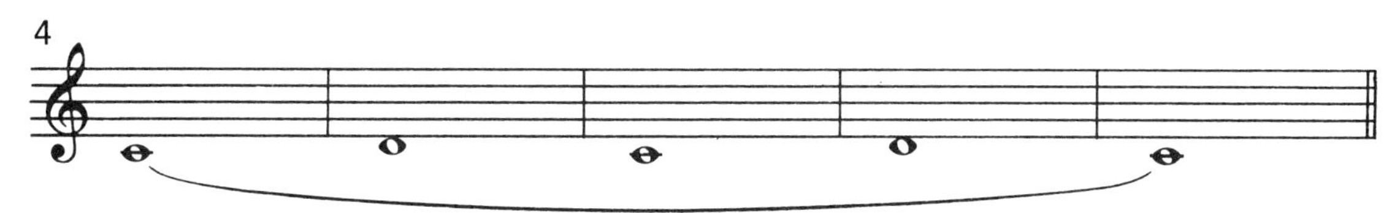

Curved lines found under or over the music are called 'Slurs' and the notes within them are played smoothly and in one breath, without use of the tongue. (Don't confuse them with tied notes).

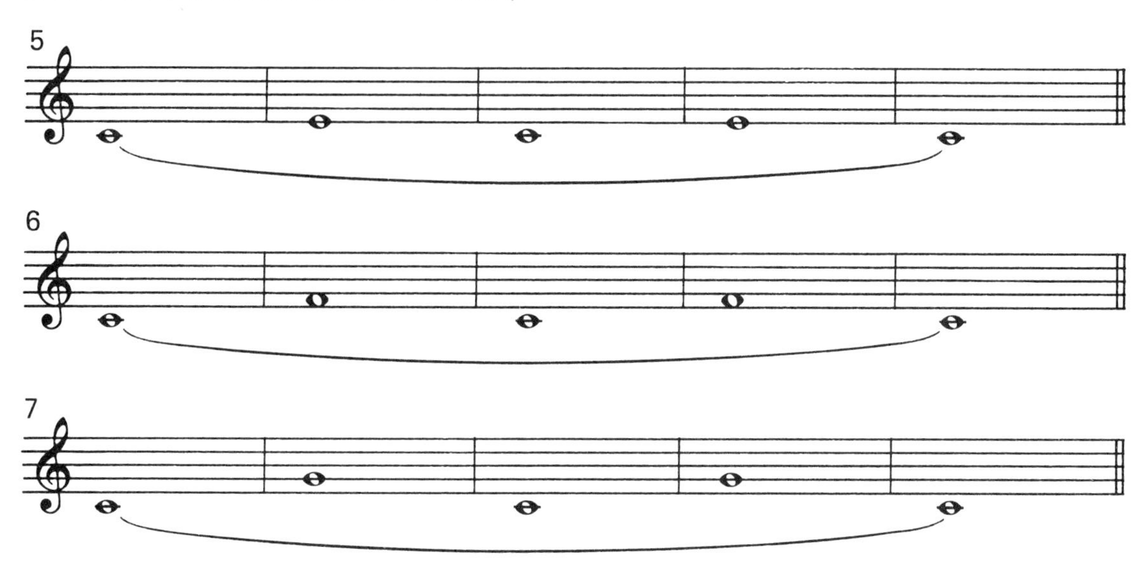

The exercises will feel difficult to begin with (and probably sound it too!) but persevere.

Points to remember:

(a) Play softly and evenly.

(b) Support the notes with a firm steady column of air.

(c) Tighten the lip for the higher intervals — but don't press the mouthpiece into your top lip to achieve results (now or ever!) or increase playing pressure.

(d) *Listen to yourself.* Does the exercise sound cleanly executed and musical? Try for this at all times (Golden Rule no. 2).

Now some more to try (not too soon! Make sure the first ones are within your grasp first). No valves all the way, of course!

Further flexibilities

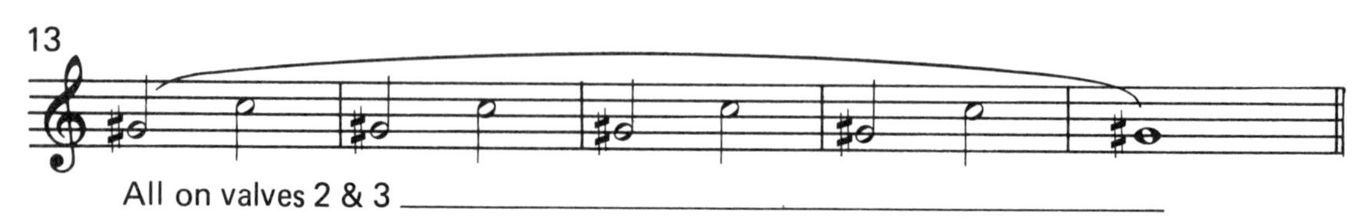

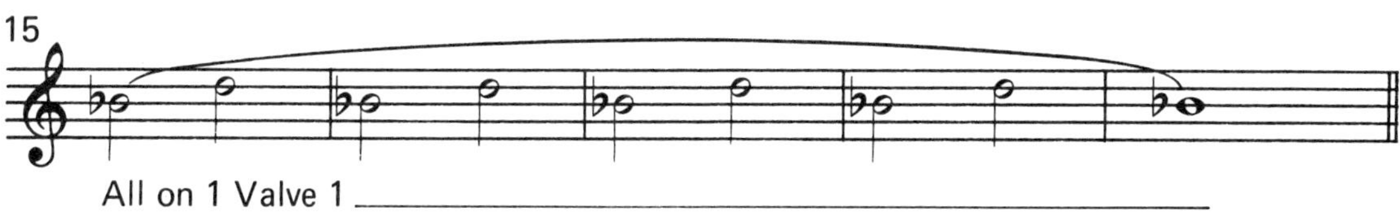

Then *only* when you feel comfortable try these:

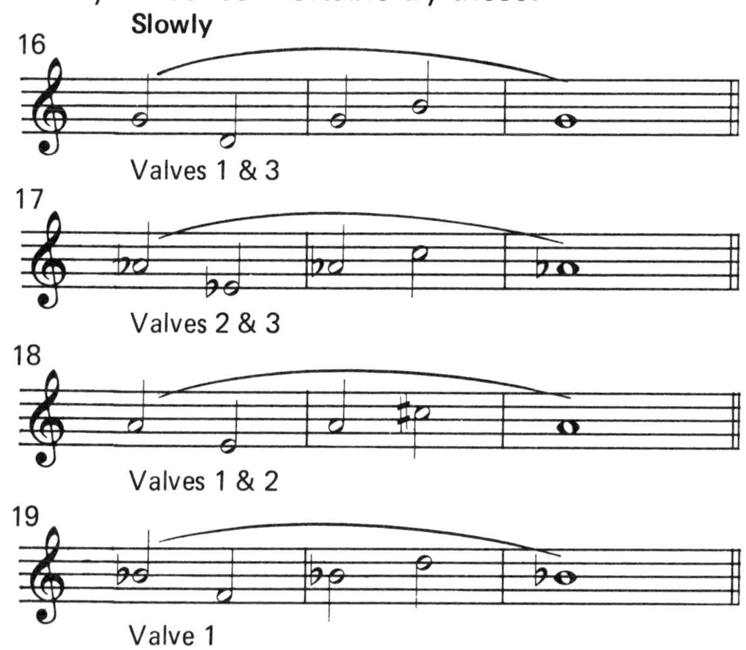

Another one:

As you progress add further intervals to the exercises — *gradually*! For example, exercise 16 on page 73 *could* be played:

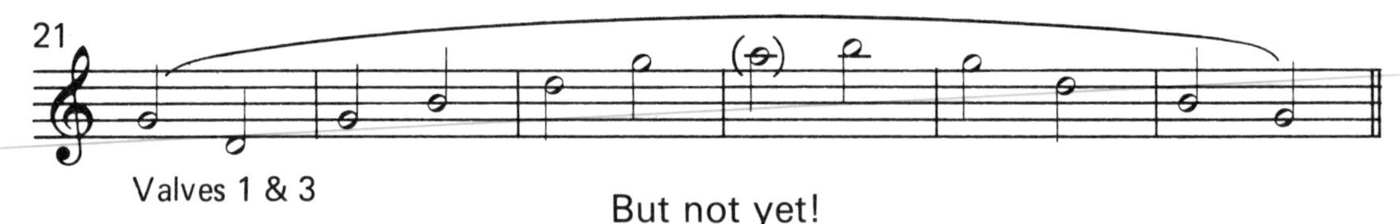

But not yet!

GOLDEN RULE 11

When practising lip slurs — let your diaphragm, air supply and lip muscles do all the work. Never shift your lip position, or press too hard — that defeats the purpose of the exercise. Another *golden rule* is: don't neglect *tonguing* for lip slurring exercises — otherwise your tongue may get 'lazy' and out of practice. Tackle lip slurs and tonguing exercises regularly each practice session.

More about bars (musical!)

As we know bar lines (or bars as the Americans call them) are used to mark out sections of music in a score. Sometimes however you may see a *double* bar line, like this:

The composer uses these to indicate the beginning or end of one section of music within another, and to mark the end of a piece of music once and for all he uses a thin-thick line like this:

If the composer wants to repeat a section of music without writing it all out again he uses a double bar line with dots like this:

When you arrive at the repeat bar look back until you find another double line with dots facing the other way like this:

and then play all the music between the two again. So:

is the same as:

23

Sometimes you will meet a first or second-time bar. They look — and work — like this:

1. 2.

1 2 3 4 5

First time, play bars 1 2 3 & 4; second time play bars 1 2 3 & 5

A way to indicate a repeated bar in shorthand is with this sign

which means 'repeat everything in the last bar again' or this one

which means 'repeat everthing in the last *two* bars again!'

Tunes to play

'John Peel!'

'Bluebells of Scotland'

'Coming Round The Mountain'

'Drink To Me Only'

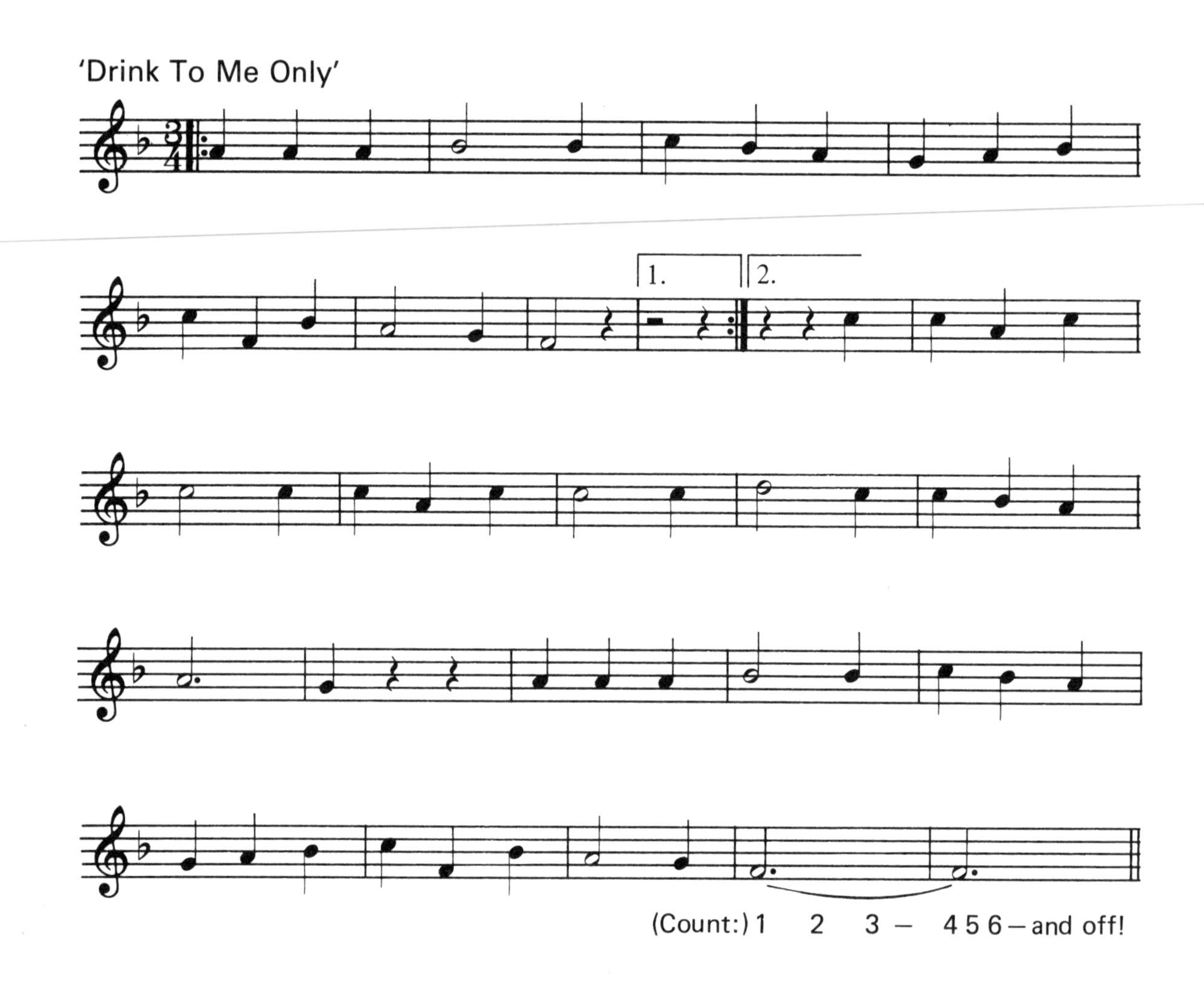

UNIT 11 New Note E

Our new note is E. Warm up first with buzzing and reference to past exercises.

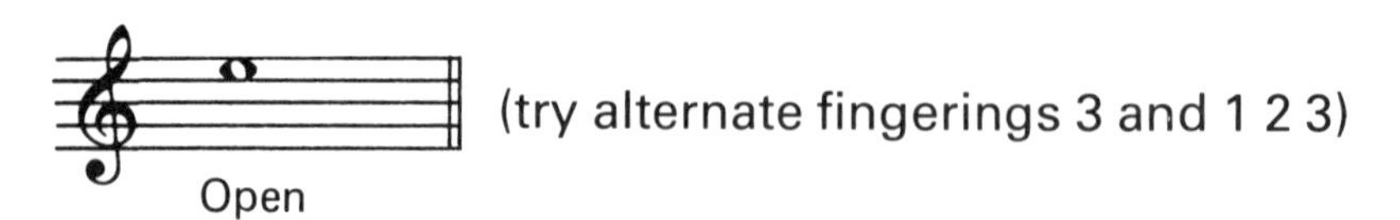

Now a long note, carrying on according to our 'golden rule' for as long as comfortable:

and if all is well, the focussing exercises.

3

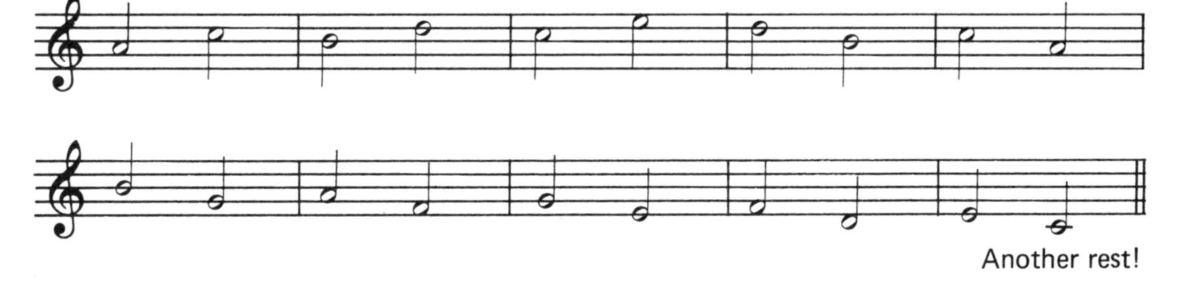

Why the frequent rests?

With notes D, E, F and G we are playing on what I call the 'embouchure bridge'. Below C (on the third space of the stave) we generally play with a relaxed 'natural' embouchure while above G (resting on the top line) we'll be playing — eventually — on the developed and flexed embouchure muscles. Between notes C and G the muscles are in a transitional state, preparing to move from their relaxed low register position into the flexed state they adopt for the upper (this is why so many students find the last hurdle to notes above G so difficult). So when producing the notes C to G we must take things easy and allow regular rest periods — because the embouchure is neither fully flexed for high note action nor fully relaxed. So, a quick 'golden rule'.

GOLDEN RULE 12

Relax, while you're crossing the bridge!

A good way to relax your lip — and strangely enough to strengthen it for high note work — is to play *low* notes!

Low notes

These four new notes take us to the bottom of the legitimate trumpet register.

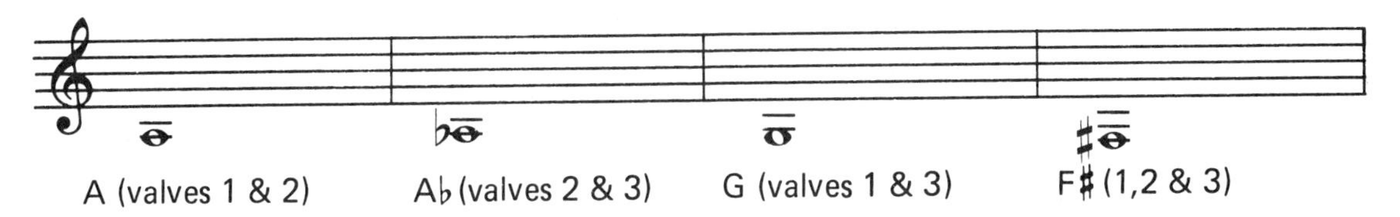

To begin with these notes may sound fuzzy and feel hard to produce. Don't worry and keep practising them gently, like this:

a) Play down to each note from low C. Start with A, and when you have controlled the note, repitch it (using the tongue if you can), then hold the note for as long as comfortable. Remember: don't force volume — just produce the note as well as you naturally can to begin with. If it dies — just relax and try again.

RIGHT EMBOUCHURE FOR LOW NOTES!

b) Don't reposition the embouchure or tilt the trumpet to help the note along.

WRONG EMBOUCHURE FOR LOW NOTES!

c) Don't roll your bottom lip out into the mouthpiece to make things easier.

d) Make sure that no undue pressure is being passed onto your top lip.

Now some simple exercises!

Long notes, or as long as possible! Don't expect miracles right away.

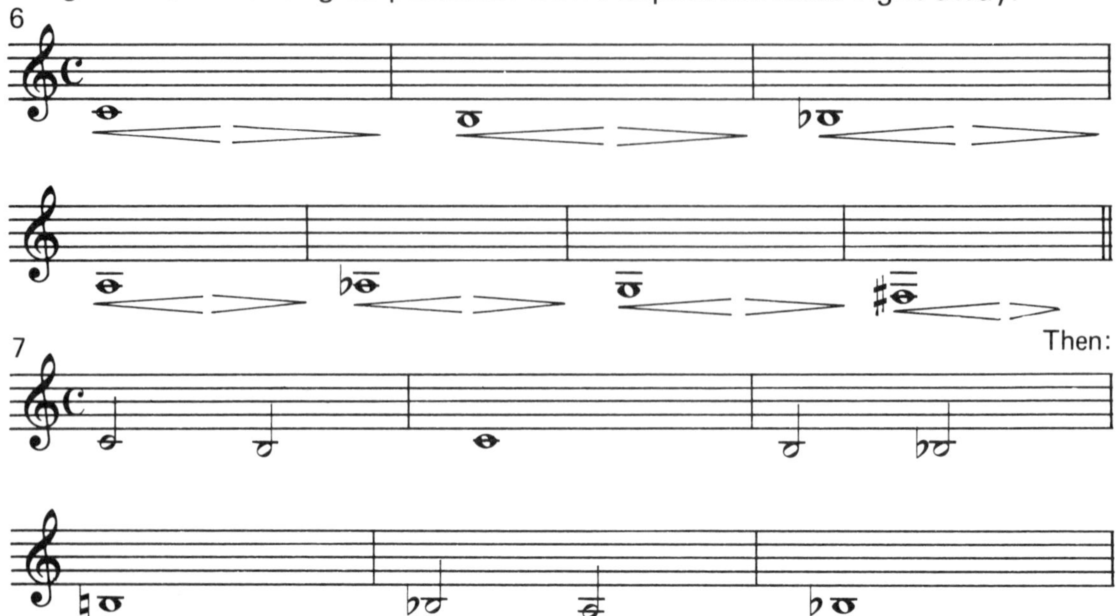

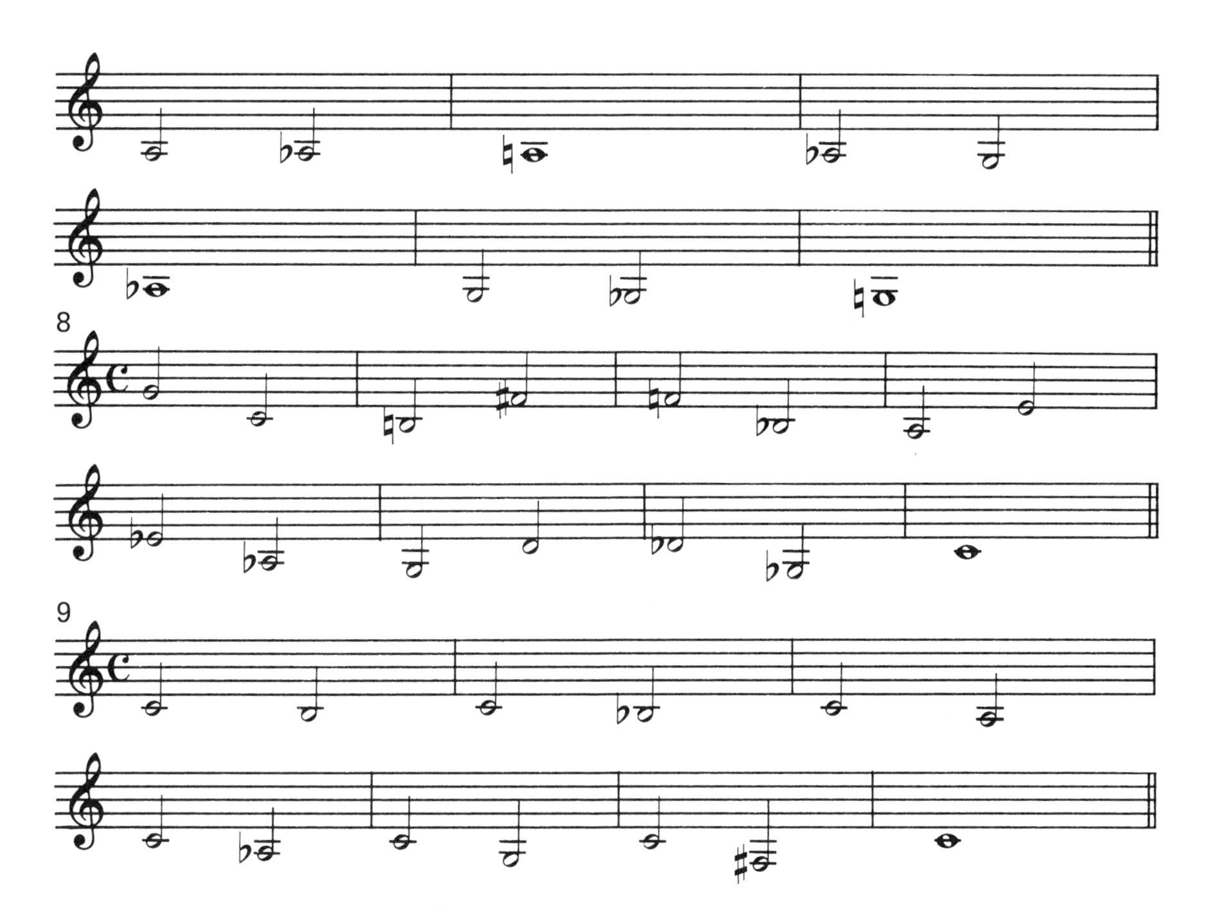

Practise low notes daily. Try to develop the idea of playing them with a wide open throat, so that the column of air with which you support your note production is at its widest for the bottom register. A warm, round and satisfying tone will be the (enviable) result:

GOLDEN RULE 13

Don't try to force a big sound when playing in the trumpet's bottom register. Your lip muscles have to get used to playing down there — and as with most areas of trumpet playing, regular and unhurried practice will pay the best dividends!

Pedal notes

. . . are a lengthy study in themselves. To get used to the subterranean trumpet register slacken your lip completely *without altering your embouchure structure* and try and produce any legitimate note or sound, at least one octave below bottom C. The notes are there — but your lip will have to get used to producing them. Pedal notes are easier on a fluëgelhorn — try it sometime.

Tunes to play

'Swanee River'

'All Through The Night'

'Battle Hymn Of The Republic'

UNIT 12 New Note F

New note F. Warm up thoroughly and try it. and F♯

Valve 1 Valve 2

Now try a long note without playing too long and straining.

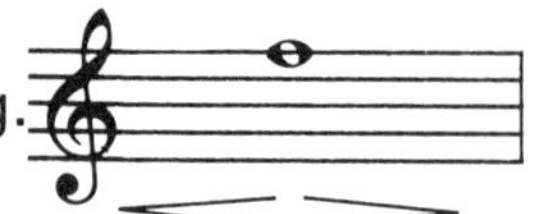

The scale of F

Key signature — 1 flat (B♭ as we know).

1

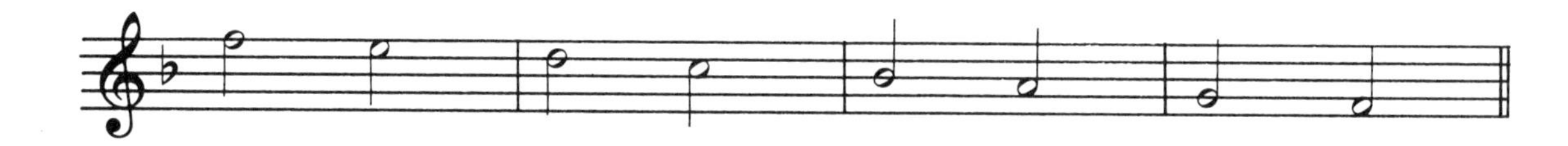

Now try the exercises:

2

3

4
Rest!
Tunes to play
'Country Song'
'King's A' Comin''

'Early One Morning'
'Barbara Allen'
'The Marseillaise'
'The Londonderry Air'

'Oh Susanna'

The Natural

Sometimes a note is flattened or sharpened automatically. For example in the key of G the note F will always be sharpened because F occurs in the key signature.

Again in this bar of music

the last B will be flattened automatically as once a note is designated flat or sharp within one bar it will be flattened or sharpened each time within that bar.

If the composer needs to avoid this happening he uses a natural (♮) sign. This restores the note to its normal pitch and cancels out all other rules.

Try this exercise:

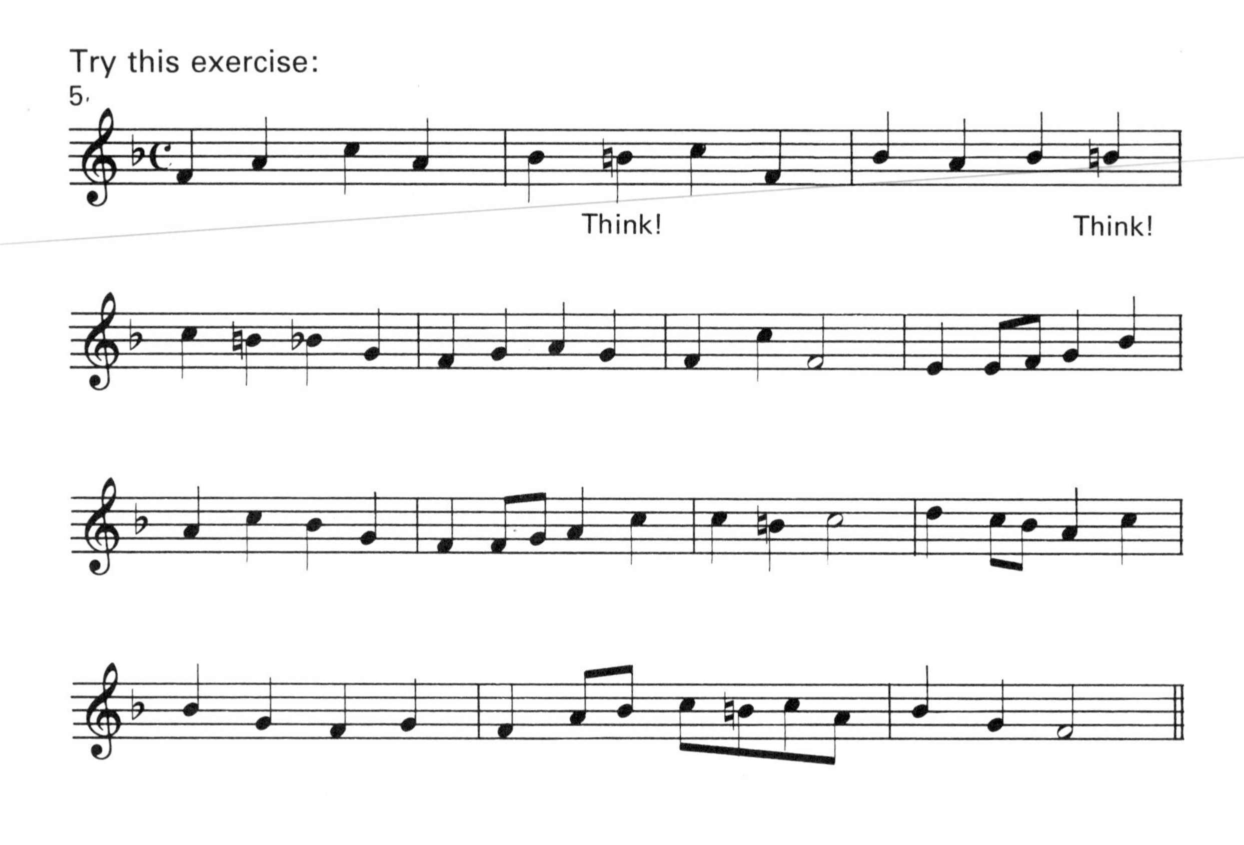

UNIT 13 New note G

As usual warm up thoroughly before playing this note. Remember our golden rules!

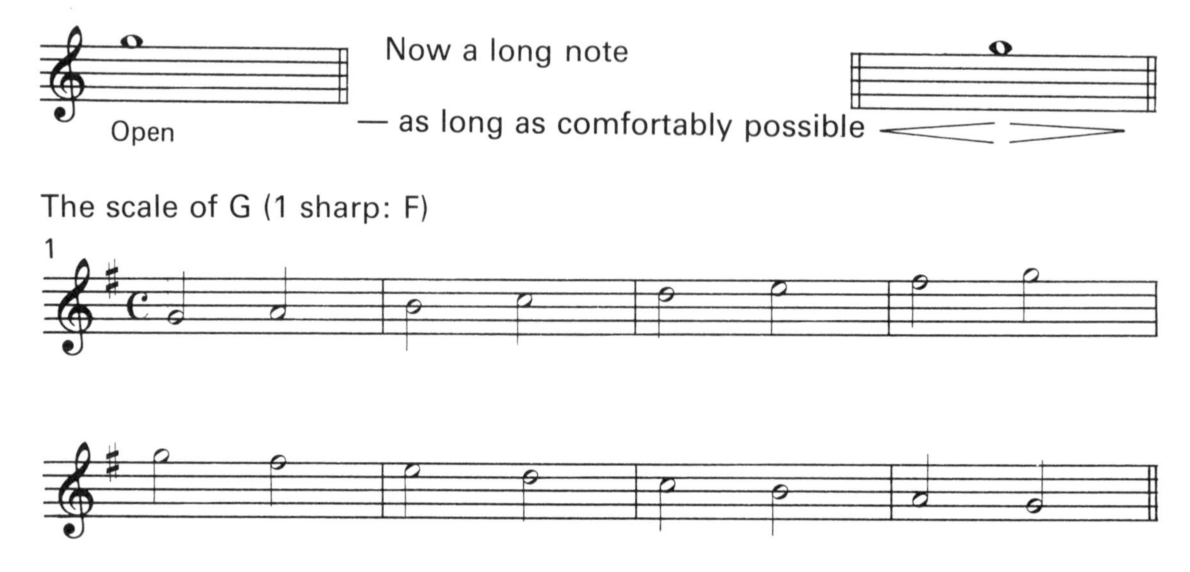

The upper register

Most beginner's books stop short at or around the note G. This is because notes above G are more difficult and require a very well trained embouchure for their production. To get ready for playing in the top register, however, practise:

a) Buzzing

b) Long low notes, regularly

c) All the flexibility exercises in this book

d) All the rest of the exercises!

Here are the fingerings for top notes to high C:

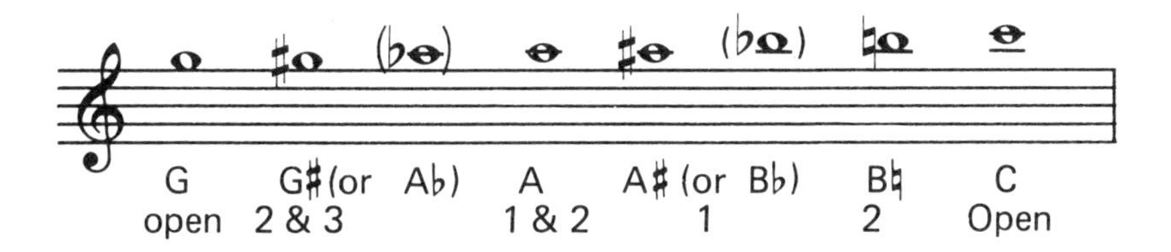

Before tackling them make sure

a) That your embouchure feels healthy, springy and ready.

b) That production in the lower and middle register is confident, tonally good, and *feels* easy.

c) That you have taken the advice of your teacher.

When tackling top notes:

a) Focus the note carefully.

b) Support it with a controlled narrow stream of air from the diaphragm.

c) Think 'tee' or 'dee' during production.

d) Make sure the note is produced via your lip muscles — not by brute force and ignorance.

e) Take regular rests, and **never** force notes.

GOLDEN RULE 14

Remember that trumpet top notes are supported by a well-developed and in-trim embouchure, and with the air flow controlled by your diaphragm. For a parallel, think of water from a garden hose . . . and think of the hose-nozzle as your embouchure. As the nozzle (or your embouchure!) tightens, the water (or your airflow!) should narrow, from a broad generous stream to a tight intense jet. The process of thinking 'ee' as opposed to 'oo' helps to effect this change — and makes a vital difference in note production.

UNIT 14

Further thoughts...

In the last section of the book I've briefly discussed some other key issues in trumpet playing — not all of them covered in books elsewhere and, I hope, of interest to trumpeters everywhere.

By now you should be visiting a teacher regularly and dipping into other books as well; standard tutors like Arban, and Langey, trumpet textbooks like Delbert Dales's 'Trumpet Technique' (if you can find a copy), and books of exercises by specialists such as Max Schlossberg, Charles Colin, Harold Mitchell and Bill Bay. Listening to all kinds of good trumpeters on record or in person is vital too. A 'Golden Rule' won't come amiss here.

GOLDEN RULE 15

Experience and enjoyment are the keys to improvement.

UNIT 15

Warming up

'Warming up' — getting the trumpet and embouchure used to each other again before practice or performance — is a vital preliminary. Nevertheless players new to the game — and sometimes fulltime professionals — often forget about it; an omission which can badly affect what comes after.

Any strenuous activity normally requires a warm-up. Weightlifters flex their muscles and breathe deeply. Long distance runners and sprinters trot around the track. Singers practise scales. The idea is to prepare the body for the stress ahead — in the same way that a motorist turns his car engine over gently before revving up and speeding off down the freeway. For a trumpet player's sensitive embouchure the act of playing is just as taxing as a marathon. The tiny lip muscles — constantly flexed tight, then relaxed in a second, and often forced to work when rest is necessary — can easily be strained if they're not previously loosened into a supple state before taxing exercises and playing routines are tackled.

So a warm-up routine is essential for all levels of performance. Before practice I recommend the following:

(a) Buzz the lips, to wake them up.

(b) Warm the instrument up by blowing air through it.

(c) *Without using the tongue* try to produce C or G in the low register.

(d) When the note you want is coming easily, try producing it *using the tongue this time.*

(e) Introduce chromatics, *gradually* widening the interval (say just C to E, first line, to begin with), and stopping for a break immediately if the notes dry up, or strain is felt.

(f) Finally limber up with ascending scales and chromatics, C to C, F to F, and so on.

This routine should be spread over a couple of minutes at most. For more advanced players I recommend a more thorough warm-up still, which can comfortably last ten minutes at least.

GOLDEN RULE 16

Your lip muscles will always let you know when they're awake, and ready to tackle a full workout. Before then, carefully monitor the progress of your warm-up routine. If a note dries up, or even feels unduly hard, you're getting a message from your lip, 'Wait for it! I'm not awake yet!' Let the sleepy muscles call the tune as they wake up. If you wait for them, they'll work better for you afterwards.

The cool off

Cooling off the lip muscles after practice or performance is a far less widely adopted practice. But it's a good idea and once again there's a strong sporting parallel to be drawn. After stressful activity most sportsmen build in a de-tensing period — very often with a thorough relaxing massage.

Exactly the same privileges, I think, should be extended to the trumpeter's lip, so that when the next playing period is due you can start in where you left off — after a warm up of course!

GOLDEN RULE 17
Leave your lip as you would wish to find it! — with a gentle massage.

This is how to do it:

Make sure practice or performance ends with long relaxing low notes (see p. 80) or pedal tones, allowing any strain or stress to reflect naturally in the sound and relaxing the pressure further, accordingly. Try to leave your lip feeling relaxed and lively — not bruised, dry and inflexible. Then things will be even better next time!

UNIT 16

Practice: The golden do's and dont's

Do's

(a) Do practise regularly. Ten minutes a day is far better than two hours once a week — long irregular practice periods only strain the lip. A little work (say five minutes a day) trains the embouchure sensibly and gradually.

(b) Do practise while you're mentally and physically fresh. In the morning is a good time.

(c) Do practise constructively, by setting up a routine. A sensible one for the advanced student might be — in this order —warm-up (2 mins), scales (5 mins), long notes (5 mins), tonguing (10 mins), lip flexibilities (10 mins), studies (30 mins). But see (d)!

(d) Do **Rest** regularly during practice. Leave sensible gaps (a minute or two) between exercises to give your lip time to recover its bounce. Straining the lip in the cause of hard work is counter productive and will just slow you up.

(e) Do listen to yourself at all times. And be a tough critic. But don't forget to pat yourself on the back when things are sounding good too!

(f) Do be adventurous. Keep on the lookout for new music to practise and have fun with new challenges.

(g) Do practise everything slowly first — and rhythmically, with a metronome if you have one. Playing at speed can hide faults in execution and embouchure. And sloppy time keeping will make whatever you play sound poor.

(h) Do select a nice airy room, with comfortable accoustics. Too many curtains and carpets will dull your sound discouragingly, but too much echo can hide faults too. Find a happy medium.

And the Dont's

(a) Don't practise too much. Remember that ten fresh keen minutes a day are better than forty minutes of reluctant uphill grind.

(b) Don't practise with a mute, unless you have to (see p. 21).

(c) Don't always practise familiar exercises. This is very useful for keeping the lip in trim — but practice should also involve attempting new things, making mistakes — and improving!

(d) Don't make the mistake of thinking that practice must *sound* good. It ought to sound dreadful quite often — ironing out faults is the key to improvement.

GOLDEN RULE 18

Remember that trumpet playing is to be enjoyed. Never let practice turn into a chore — vary your routine, take a break, buy some new exercises. Of course nothing comes easily — including trumpet playing. But don't let that prevent you enjoying the trip!

UNIT 17

Positioning the mouthpiece on your lip

Most teachers and instruction books assume — quite correctly — that the young player will position his mouthpiece at the exact centrepoint of his lips. This is sound logic, based on a sensible premise; that the embouchure muscles should all gravitate to a central point — the mouthpiece — and that equal muscular strength on either side provides the maximum potential strength for performance.

The majority of good performers usually do, or appear to possess a 'classic' central embouchure, although close examination proves that some of our greatest players have actually cultivated lip positions which, for the sake of comfort are several centimetres or more off centre. My belief is that no 'golden rule' can be applied to all players. And the object of these few paragraphs is to take a second look at the rule of playing 'dead-centre', and perhaps to lay a ghost that can otherwise haunt beginners — and sometimes advanced players too!

To begin with, most trumpet-players who play on an absolutely central embouchure probably do so by accident, not design. Many physical features — the structure of your jaw, lower and upper teeth, even the thickness of the lips — can have a controlling effect on where your mouthpiece finishes up. And front teeth — very often slightly irregular at least — are often the governing factors necessitating an off-centre bias. In short a lot of valuable time can be wasted trying to combat practical physical impediments with a text-book ideal theory. My advice would be: *'position the mouthpiece as closely as possible to the centre of the lips consistent with comfort and playing-ease'*. Very often, slightly away from the centre the mouthpiece will suddenly seem to 'click' into a comfortable 'seated' position.

It might be a salutary exercise to look at a picture of Alison McFadyen, (our model, a professional trumpet player) and her natural embouchure setting, as against the setting of our author — but be warned! While it may be that rules are occasionally bendable, *beginners must always adopt as nearly central a position as possible.*

And one rider, which I add from personal experience and advice from a lot of good players too. If you have adopted an unorthodox position and then set an embouchure successfully within it despite the fact — don't change, stay where you are. I believe that it's extremely difficult to reset an embouchure in a quite different position, and that trying (I tried for four years without success) can result in depression and loss of morale. Most experienced trumpet players say,'if the results are satisfactory and comfortable, then stay where you are'. And ignore the off-centre comments!

The last point (usually from worriers) is, 'well, I'm playing well but would things be even better if my embouchure were dead central'. In my opinion the answer is probably 'no' — for if your central lip position was so perfect why did you move to begin with? To satisfy yourself though, take the advice of one or two experienced ears. Above all, don't worry. *Worry and pressure are the worst handicaps in that most mentally based of physical pursuits — playing the trumpet.*

GOLDEN RULE 19

'The power of positive thinking' is vital to good trumpet playing. Worry or mental strain can affect every area of your performance. A simple doubt such as 'Will I hit that top note at the end of the piece?' sometimes — perversely — means that you don't. More serious long term problems (such as embouchure position) can turn into complexes, and bring even a seasoned player to his knees. So — first check the results you are achieving. Are they successful? If you seriously feel that the answer's 'no', then consult a first-class teacher — talking out a problem will help. Above all remember that problems are there to be beaten. You *can* do it.

UNIT 18

Keeping fit

Good health is as vital to trumpet players as it is to everyone else. However a large amount of discussion has taken place over the years suggesting that good trumpet players need to be *extra* fit. At first glance the idea seems reasonable and why it does — and whether it really *is* reasonable — is worth a look.

Everyone from childhood onwards is conditioned with the idea that trumpets are harder to blow than almost anything else. 'You'll need a lot of puff for that!' is the view of most people who don't play: probably they remember the traditional cartoon of the trumpeter — eyes popping, cheeks bulging, seizure-bent. It's a fallacy of course — the trained player knows that playing a trumpet correctly is not much harder than a penny-whistle. And therefore there's no reason why a strenuous keep-fit routine should be necessary. Most professional trumpeters recognise the fact and acknowledge it by continuing to play well without visiting the gym daily.

What is vital of course is normally-good physical and mental health. To play the trumpet well you should feel healthily up to par, *and mentally alert, rested and happy.* The trumpet — more than any other instrument — responds to general well-being, physical and mental, and once this has gone your playing may be at serious risk.

Circular breathing

. . . is a very popular technique and by no means a new one. It's widely used among jazz musicians — sometimes for show, and sometimes because it's an invaluable way of negotiating very long improvised lines.

Briefly the method involves inhaling air through the nose, and retaining simultaneously a supply of air in the cheeks which is constantly replenished and then fed through the mouthpiece. The result is that — to all intents and purposes — the player can continue blowing indefinitely and without (apparently) pausing for breath.

The effect is spectacular and has been widely adopted, but buy an instruction book to make sure you learn correctly.

UNIT 19
Jazz and improvisation

Improvisation is an important area of music making of great value in ear training and harmonic awareness. It was — and is still — the distinguishing factor in jazz music (jazz musicians are often said to be the most skilled improvisers of all) but plenty of other music forms — rock and pop music, rhythm and blues, country and western and some contemporary classical music — incorporate improvisation as a matter of course.

'Improvisation' is 'making it up as you go along' — playing by ear and not from the music. Usually — though not always — the technique is based on the chords and harmonies of the music being played, and if you can whistle a tune of your own above the harmonies of another by ear, the chances are you can improvise just as easily on an instrument.

To find out how this is done, let's take a simple chord of C, and having noted its make up:

Play up and down the chord on the trumpet or piano. Now play the notes of the chord in any melodic and rhythmic order, as set out in this exercise:

Now do the same thing for yourself. Congratulations. You are now improvising (vertically — or up and down the chord notes) on the chord of C.

Try the same exercise with these chords:

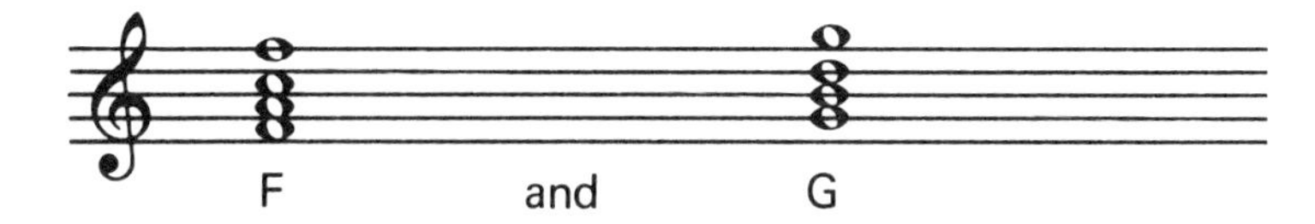

and practise these chords for a while until you are used to their makeup, and what they sound like.

Good. Now we're ready to try improvising on the most famous chord sequence of all, the 12 bar blues. In the key of C this is made up of the three chords we have studied, in twelve bar-long patterns. The F and G chords will have a dominant 7th added to make the chord correct so add an Eb to the F A and C of the F chord, and an F♮ to the G B and D of the G chord.

Use the technique we have perfected to play the blues like this:

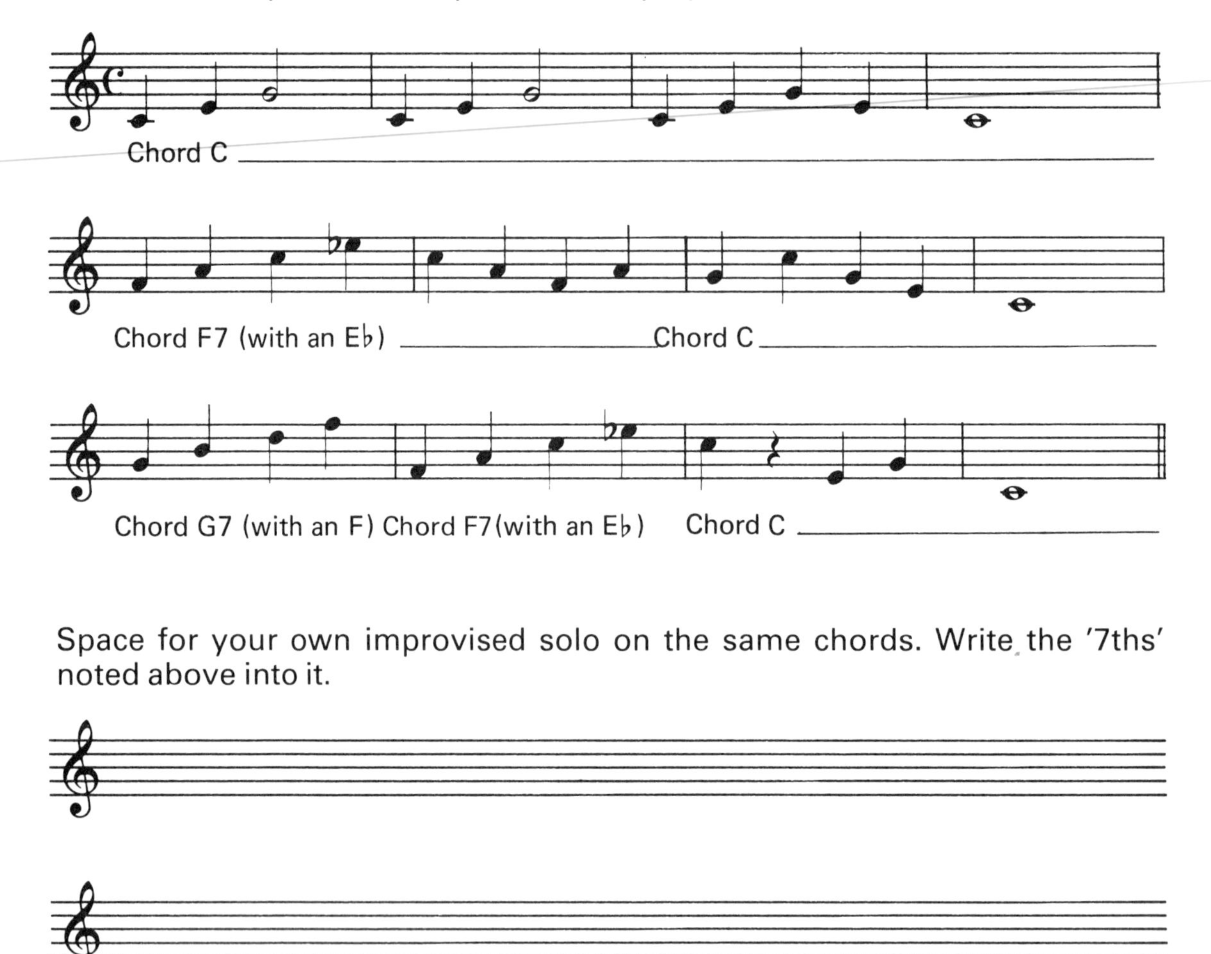

Space for your own improvised solo on the same chords. Write the '7ths' noted above into it.

Good! To strengthen and enrich our improvisation we need to think about developing it rhythmically and melodically.

Rhythmically

Try the same exercise again, but this time try and break up the notes you play into slightly more ambitious rhythmic patterns like this:

Try playing the example, and hear how much more interesting it sounds. Then make up your own solo in the same way:

Good.

...And melodically

When we improvise this time we need to make the improvisation more melodic. A good way to do this is by using not just the three notes of the basic chord, but the eight notes of the *scale* of the chord. Look at bar 5. The chord is F7 – and we can use any note in the scale of F accordingly (substituting an Eb – the dominant 7th of the chord – for the normal E♮). This is known as 'horizontal' (as opposed to 'vertical') improvisation. Generally the primary notes of the chord (the root, third and fifth) will sound better if they are central to the phrase you make up — your ear will tell you when this doesn't happen. But other notes from the scale can now be introduced to embellish your creation. And as your ear gains in confidence more and more notes from the scale can be introduced.

Here's an example:

Now write one for yourself, on the same chords again.

The same principles apply to any chord sequence. As you look at more difficult sequences use the checklist of chords beneath to help you — and remember that, in whatever key they appear, the structure of a basic chord is *exactly the same*. Just apply the structures beneath to the relevant notes and key.

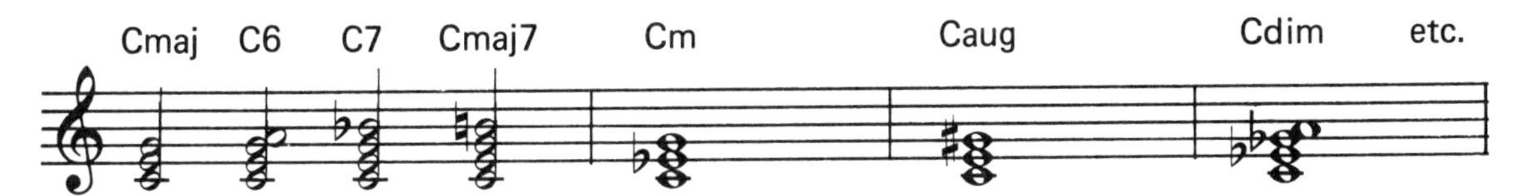

There are numerous aids to improvisation: books, tapes and records (which supply you with melodies, sequences and pre-recorded rhythm section against which to practise) and best of all — regularly organised seminars and workshops countrywide. And one of the best ways of improving of course is to listen to good improvisers at work, on records, TV, radio and 'live'. A lovely way to spend your spare time — or perhaps your life.

Good luck!

Some final theory to remember

This sign 𝄋

When you see a sign above the music like this

remember where it is. Later you will meet the instruction 'Da 𝄋 al 𝄌' which means 'play from the 𝄋 **again** up to the coda sign 𝄌' (you'll see another instruction 'to 𝄌 coda'). Then you jump to the coda sign 𝄌 and play all the music after the coda sign!

i.e.

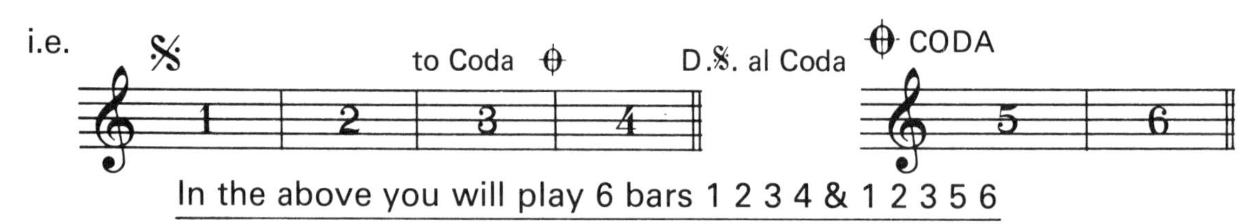

In the above you will play 6 bars 1 2 3 4 & 1 2 3 5 6

Fine means finish

Degrees of speed are shown as follows:

Andante **Adagio** **Lento**	Slow
Moderato **Mod.**	Medium
Allegro **Presto**	Quick

To speed up or slow down the following terms are used:

Rallentando **Rall** **Ritard.** **Rit.**	Slow Down	**Accelerando** **Accel.**	Go Quicker

Pause = 𝄐 Accent = > ʌ

All the notes and valve positions

Bibliography

ARBAN, J B — Cornet Method (Boosey & Hawkes)
ARMSTRONG, LOUIS – Music Makers (IMP)
ARMSTRONG, LOUIS – Trumpet Solos (IMP)
ARMSTRONG, LOUIS – 50 Dixieland Classics
BERLE, A. — How to create and develop a jazz solo (Mel Bay)
DALE, DELBERT – Trumpet Technique (OUP)
D'ATH, NORMAN – Cornet Playing (Boosey & Hawkes)
FOX, FRED – Essentials of Brass Playing (Volkwein Bros Inc. Pittsburgh)
Fun Book for Trumpet (IMP)
Fun Music for Trumpet, Books 1 & 2 (IMP)
HERFURTH, C PAUL – Tune A Day, Books 1 & 2 (Chappell)
LANGEY, OTTO — Practical Tutor for Cornet & Trumpet (Boosey & Hawkes)
Learn to Play the Bb Trumpet/Cornet – A two-hour video lesson, introduced by Richard Baker. Produced by Domestic Video Services
MITCHELL, HAROLD – Mitchell on Trumpet, Books 1 to 4 (Hansen)
RIDGEON, JOHN – Brass for Beginners (Boosey & Hawkes)
SENIOR, RODNEY – An introduction to Trumpet & Cornet (EMI)
SCHLOSSBERG – Lip Flexiblities
Trumpet Fancies (IMP)
Trumpet Magic, Books 1 & 2 (IMP)
Trumpet Showcase (IMP)
Trumpet Time, Books 1 & 2 (IMP)
WASTALL, PETER – Learn As You Play: Trumpet & Cornet (Boosey & Hawkes)